מִתְקַדֵּם
Mitkadem
Hebrew Language For Youth

RAMAH 2

Student Workbook

By Cheri Ellowitz Silver

Illustrations by Mira Scharf
Designed by Edmon J. Rodman

UAHC Press
New York, New York

This Mitkadem Workbook belongs to: _____

To my first Hebrew teachers:
Eva Perlmutter Schwartz
Cantor David Grunberger
Edith Glattstein Schwartz
Yitzhak Goodman
I am honored to pass down their dedication to Talmud Torah.
— C.E.S.

Mitkadem
Hebrew Language For Youth
Ramah 2
Student Workbook

Development of the *Mitkadem: Hebrew language for Youth* curriculum
has been made possible through the generous support
of the Gilbert Tilles Endowment Fund.
Additional funding has been provided by the Feldman Library Fund,
a gift of the Milton and Sally Feldman Foundation
in memory of Sally Feldman.

UAHC
PRESS
For a Lifetime
of Jewish Learning

Manufactured in the United States of America.
10 9 8 7 6 5 4 3 2 1

INTRODUCTION

Hi! Welcome to Ramah 2 of the Mitkadem program. Remember me from Ramah 1? I'm Mitty. I'll be helping you learn to read Hebrew.

There are other helpers that go with this book. You will find them in your Hebrew Helpers Kit. Use them whenever you see these signs:

- ▢ *Alef-bet Letter Cards*
- ▮ *Advancer Vowel Cards*
- ▮ *Alef Advancer*

Answers to all activities in this book are in the back. I'll tell you where to find them at the right time.

In the back of this book there are also awards for finishing each lesson. Every time you earn one, take it home. Keep them in a special envelope, until you have them all. When you stack them all together, they form a Mitty flip book!

In Ramah 1 you learned:
1. About the shapes of the Hebrew letters.
2. That we read Hebrew from right to left.
3. Some Hebrew words, like:

Shabbat שַׁבָּת   *Shofar* שׁוֹפָר

All of the Hebrew letters that you learned are **consonants**. Now you are ready for Ramah 2.

On Your Own

Review the Hebrew letters. You can:

1 Take out your *Alef-bet Letter Cards*. ▢ Identify the sound and name of each letter. You can do this alone or with a friend. If there is a letter that you don't know, use the *Alef-bet chart* on the *Hebrew Helpers Kit* envelope for help.

2 Do the "What's the Difference?" Puzzles in your Hebrew Helpers Kit. Have fun!

3 Use your *Alef Advancer* ▮ to test yourself on the sound and name of the letters.

(Don't worry if you can't remember them all! All of the letters will be reviewed in this workbook.)

CONSONANTS AND VOWELS

In English, consonants and vowels look the same. Both consonants and vowels are necessary to spell a word. They fit into the word together. For example:

Some English **consonants** are: b c d h m r s

English **vowels** are: a e i o u

Some words made from the letters above are: **bed   more   ice   hum**

You can't write English words without the vowels.

They would look like this: **bd   mr   c   hm**

With Hebrew we CAN read words without vowels. The entire Torah scroll is written without vowels! Hebrew newspapers and books are written without vowels.

> VOWELS ARE HELPERS IN HEBREW.
> They help us figure out how to pronounce a word.

These are holiday words that you know with and without vowels:

WITHOUT VOWELS	WITH VOWELS
Purim פרים	*Purim* פּוּרִים
Rosh HaShanah ראש השנה	*Rosh HaShanah* רֹאשׁ הַשָׁנָה
Sukkot סכת	*Sukkot* סֻכּוֹת

Circle the parts of the words above that ARE VOWELS.

In Ramah 2 you will learn how to read Hebrew words using vowels as helpers.

Answers for this lesson are on page 74. When you finish this lesson, take home your award!

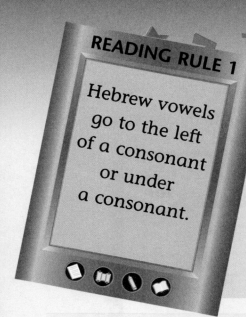

READING RULE 1

Hebrew vowels go to the left of a consonant or under a consonant.

Take out these letters from your *Alef-bet Letter Cards*: ▢

shin שׁ   fei פ   reish ר

Sounds like SH   Sounds like F   Sounds like R

Find the *Advancer Vowel Cards* ▨ in your Hebrew Helpers Kit. They fit right over the *Alef-bet Letter Cards* ▢. Try it!

You can see that VOWELS go:

Under the consonant letters   שֶׁ שֵׁ   שֶׁ   פֶ פֵ   רָ רַ   ַ

To the left of the consonant letters

פֵ פוּ שׁוֹ שׁוּ ר רוּ

The first vowels you will learn are:

VOWEL	WHERE?	NAME OF VOWEL	SOUND
וֹ	*To the left* of the consonant	cholam	**OH** Like in *shofar*
ָ	*Under* consonant	kamatz	**AH** Like in *matzah*

Take these two *Advancer Vowel Cards* ▨ out and return the rest to your Hebrew Helpers Kit. Using the letter and vowel cards you have out, put together these Hebrew SYLLABLES. When we make the sound, we say the consonant FIRST and the vowel SECOND.

SHOH שׁוֹ   FOH פוּ   ROH רוֹ

SHAH שָׁ   FAH פָ   RAH רָ

Now use your cards to put together this word: *Shofar* שׁוֹפָר

3

READ WITH A TEACHER

REMEMBER: 1. We read Hebrew from RIGHT to LEFT.

2. Say the CONSONANT FIRST and the vowel second.

Right to Left Edition

THE HEBREW READER

1   רוּ פֿוּ רוּ שֿׁוֹ פֿוּ רוּ שֿׁוֹ שֿׁוּ

2   שָׁ רְ פְּ רָ שְׁ פְּ רָ פְּ

3   שׁוֹר שָׁשׁ שׁוֹפ שָׁ שׁוֹ שָׁ שָׁ שׁוֹ

4   שׁוֹפ פָּשׁ פוֹפ פוֹ פָּ פָּ פֿוּ

5   שָׁפ רְשׁ רוֹר רָפ רוֹ רוּ רָ

6   שׁוֹפ פוֹ פֿר שָׁשׁ רוֹפ שׁוֹר

שׁוֹפֿר
Shofar

Two syllables!

7   שׁוֹפוּ שׁוֹ-פֿוּ שׁוֹרוּ שׁוֹ-רוּ רוֹפוּ רוֹ-פֿוּ

8   שָׁרוּ שָׁ-רוּ רָשׁוּ רָ-שׁוֹ פְּשׁוֹ פָּ-שׁוֹ

9   שׁוֹ-פֿר שׁוֹפֿ שׁוֹ-פָּ פְּשׁוֹר פָּ-שׁוֹר

1 Circle the VOWELS in these Hebrew words:

Shofar שׁוֹפָר   Jerusalem יְרוּשָׁלַיִם   Torah תּוֹרָה

Challah חַלָה   Menorah מְנוֹרָה

2 Practice writing. Write each consonant and vowel **six** times:

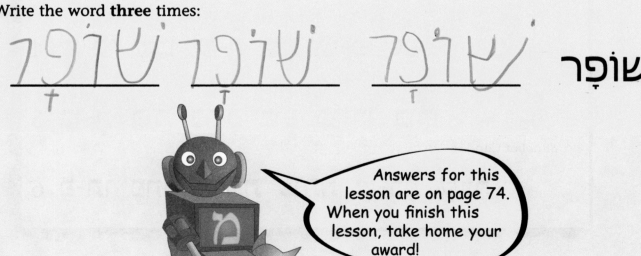

3 Write the word **three** times:

שׁוֹפָר

Answers for this lesson are on page 74. When you finish this lesson, take home your award!

Lesson 2

You know these consonants: שׁ ר פ   You know these vowels: וּ אָ

NEW consonants: בּ   תּ ת   NEW vowel: ַ
bet   tav   patach
Sounds like B   Sounds like T   Sounds like AH in *matzah*

These sounds make the word *Shabbat* שַׁבָּת.

Right to Left Edition

THE HEBREW READER

 Just for Kids

1 בַּ בָּ בַּ בּוּ בָּ בּוֹר בָּשׁ פּוֹב

2 תּוֹ תָּ תוֹ תַ תַּב תּוֹפ תָּפ שׁוֹת

3 בּוּ פַּ שַׁ פָּשׁ פַּשׁ שַׁב בַּת פּוֹת

Two syllables!

4 שַׁ־בּוּ שַׁבּוּ שַׁ־תָּ שַׁתָּ שַׁ־פַּ שַׁפַּ

5 בּוּ־תָּ בּוֹתָ בּוּ־פַּ בּוֹפַ בּוּ־רוֹ בּוֹרוֹ

6 פָּ־תוֹ פָּתוֹ פּוֹ־תָּת פּוֹתַת שַׁ־בָּת שַׁבָּת

נֵרוֹת שַׁבָּת
Shabbat Candles

On Your Own

1 Find these letters: Underline every **תּ**.
Circle every **בּ**.
Put an X on every **ר**.

כ ל בּ תּ ל נ ח כ בּ ל כ
שׁ מ ג ס ל ד בּ תּ ג פ שׁ
פ פ תּ ד י א בּ ע תּ ר תּ
ר ר ר ד נ תּ פ בּ ר ר
ג ד בּ שׁ נ נ צ ב נ ר צ
     צ   נ

2 Practice writing. Write each consonant and vowel **six** times:

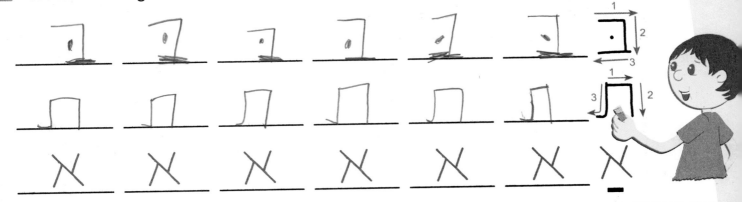

3 Use your *Alef-bet Letter Cards* ⬜ to copy these syllables:

רוֹ   בָּשׁ   פַ

Read these syllables for your teacher.

Teacher's Signature _____

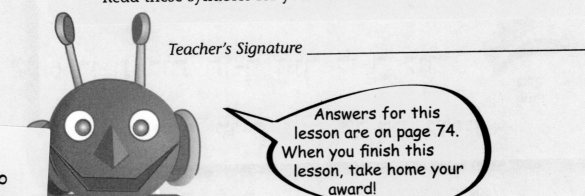

Answers for this lesson are on page 74. When you finish this lesson, take home your award!

∞

Lesson 3

You know these consonants: ב פ ר שׁ תּ ת   You know these vowels: וֹ אָ אַ

NEW consonants: ל   מ   NEW vowel: X̤

lamed   *mem*   *segol*

Sounds like **L**   Sounds like **M**   Sounds like **EH** in *melech*

READ WITH A TEACHER

REMEMBER: 1. We read Hebrew from RIGHT to LEFT. ⬅

2. Say the CONSONANT FIRST and the vowel second.

THE HEBREW READER

Just for Kids

1	לֶ לֵ לְבַ פֶּ תֵ בָּ רְ שָׁ בְּר בְּל
2	מַ מוֹ מֶ מָ מֵל מָל מוֹל מַל מֶפ
3	לַב רַב מוֹר שֶׁל רָשׁ בָּם לוֹם פוֹם
	Two syllables!
4	פֶּ-תֵ פֶּת תָּ-פַל תָּפַל תוֹ-פֶ תּוֹפֶ
5	בָּ-שֵׁ בָּשֵׁ שָׁ-בַ שָׁבַ שׁוֹ-בָּל שׁוֹבָל
6	רוּ-תָ רוּתָ תּוֹ-רְ תּוֹרְ לוּ-רְ לוּרְ
7	לְ-בַּר לְבַּר לוּ-פֶ לוּפֶ לוּ-רֵת לוּרֵת

מֶלֶךְ
King

Teacher's Signature _____

1 Practice writing. Write each consonant and vowel **six** times:

ל ל ל ל ל ל

_____ _____ _____ _____ _____ _____

_____ _____ _____ _____ _____ _____

א א א א א א א
_____ _____ _____ _____ _____ _____

2 What are the sounds and names of consonants and vowels that you know? Fill in the chart. (You can use your *Alef-bet Chart* and your *Alef Advancer* ▮ to help!)

	Consonent or Vowel	Sound	Name	Write it:
ל	C	L	*lamed*	ל
מ	C	M	Mem	א
◌ֲ	V	O	patah	—
בּ	C	B	*bet*	②
◌ָ	✓	O	*kamatz*	T
שׁ	C	Sh	Shin	שׁ
פ		F		
וֹ		OH		
ר			*reish*	

3 Match the Hebrew with the English sounds. Write the number in the blank.

1 Rah _____ בַּת   4 Bet _____ רֵשׁ

2 Loh _____ רְ   5 Mor _____ לוֹ

3 Far _____ מוֹר   6 Resh _____ פַּר

Answers for this lesson are on page 75. When you finish this lesson, take home your award!

9

READING RULE 2

Vowels cannot stand alone. Vowels have to be attached to consonants.

You know these consonants: ב ל מ פ ר שׁ ת ת

You know these vowels: וֹ אָ אַ אָ

In English, words can have vowels without consonants. Some examples are:

over **a**pple **e**lephant

In Hebrew, we can have the same sounds, but vowels cannot stand alone.

To make these sounds, we use SILENT LETTERS, like:

אֹ
Alef to create words like אוֹר *Or Light*

READ WITH A TEACHER

REMEMBER: 1. We read Hebrew from RIGHT to LEFT.

2. Say the CONSONANT FIRST and the vowel second.

Right to Left Edition

THE HEBREW READER

Just for Kids

אוֹר
Light

1 אַ אֹ אָ אֶ אַ אֹ אַ אָ אֹ

2 אֹ אוֹר אוֹל אוֹב אוֹת אוֹפ אוֹר

3 אָ אָב אַשׁ אֶשׁ אוֹת אֶל אֵל

Two syllables!

4 אַ-פֵּר אָפָר אוֹ-ל אוֹל אַ-בָּ אָבָ

5 לָ-אֵל לָאֵל פֵּ-אֶשׁ פֶּאֶשׁ תוּ-אָ תוֹאָ

6 מָ-אוֹר מָאוֹר מָאוֹר לוּ-פֵּר לוֹפֵר

Teacher's Signature _____

1 Match the sounds:

1 Ah _____   לוֹ

2 Oh _____   נֶ

3 Ah _____   אָ

4 Eh _____   אֶ

5 Loh _____   בֵ

6 Shoh _____ אוֹ

7 Bah _____   שׁוֹ

8 Beh _____   אַ

2 Take out your *Alef Advancer* ▢. Insert the two vowel strips. The opening on the right side shows syllables made with the letter **א** and different vowels. The opening on the left side shows the sounds of the syllables and the names of the vowels.

Match these syllables to their sounds. You can check your answers by looking on the back!

אָ   אֶ   אוֹ   אַ

Can you match the NAMES of these vowels, too?

3 Write the letter **six** times:

_____ _____ _____ _____ _____ _____

Answers for this lesson are on page 76. When you finish this lesson, take home your award!

Lesson 5

You know these consonants: **א ב ל מ פ ר שׁ ת ת**

You know these vowels: **וֹ אָ אֵ אֶ אֱ**

NEW consonants: **ה**   **י**   NEW vowel: **אִ**

hei   *yod*   *chirik*
Sounds like **H**   Sounds like **Y**   Sounds like **EE** in
                                            af<u>ee</u>koman

READ WITH A TEACHER

REMEMBER: 1. We read Hebrew from RIGHT to LEFT.

2. Say the CONSONANT FIRST and the vowel second.

Right to Left Edition

THE HEBREW READER   *Just for Kids*

1	הֹ וֹ הֹ הֶ הָ הֹ הֵ הָ הַ הַ	
2	יְ יֶ יֹ יֵ יִ יֶ יֹ יַ יְ יוֹ	
3	אֵל בֵּל בַּל תֵּ תָ רֵ שֵׁ מֵ פֵ לֵ אֵ בֵּ	
4	יוֹב הָא אַר יֵשׁ יָר יֵל הֵר הַב	

(Continued on Next Page)

12

THE HEBREW READER

Just for Kids

1	הַר	רַה	הֵשׁ	שֶׁה	הַף	פָּה	תַּה	הָת

2	יִל	לִי	יְפ	פִּי	יְמ	מִי	הֵמ	מֶה

3	אִי	הֶר	יָל	לֶה	פְּשׁ	יִשׁ	יַשׁ	שִׁי

תּוֹרָה
Torah

Two syllables!

| 4 | בִּי-מָה | בִּימָה | בִּי-אָה | בִּיאָה | מִי-לָה | מִילָה |

| 5 | שֶׁ-לִי | שֶׁלִי | אִ-שָׁה | אִשָׁה | תִּי-רָה | תִּירָה |

| 6 | אוֹ-רָה | אוֹרָה | תּוֹ-רָה | תּוֹרָה | תּוֹ-רַת | תּוֹרַת |

Teacher's Signature _____

13

1 Practice writing. Write each consonant and vowel **six** times:

_____ _____ _____ _____ _____ _____

_____ _____ _____ _____ _____ _____

א   א   א   א   א   אָ

Read them with a friend.

2 Take out these *Alef-bet Letter Cards*  מ ר שׁ ל בּ ת ה פ י.

Take out these *Advancer Vowel Cards* ◻ ◻ . ְ ‑ ָ וֹ. Put together

these sounds with the cards. You will use each card only once:

a)   Mar
b)   Shol
c)   Bet
d)   Heef
e)   Yah

3 Circle the syllables that rhyme in each line:

a   בַּל לְפ מְפ בֵּל בְּפ שָׁב

b   אַת הָת פַּר בָּת אוֹל אַל

c   שֶׁל מֶשׁ יֶל שֵׁשׁ אֶב יָל

d   מוֹב יָב הוֹף אוֹב יוֹב רָב

14

Remember:

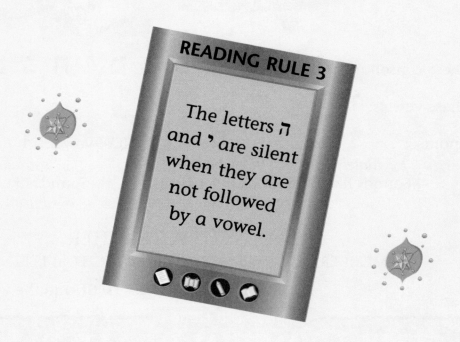

READING RULE 3

The letters ה
and ׳ are silent
when they are
not followed
by a vowel.

4 Read these syllables and words. Circle the silent consonants.

a. אוֹ פִּי יֵשׁ לָה הָל יְל לִי

b. תּוֹרָה אוֹרָה אֱמוֹר אַבָּא מִילָה

c. בִּימָה שַׁבָּת שֶׁלִּי שֶׁלּוֹ שֶׁלָּה

Answers for
this lesson are on
page 76. When you finish
this lesson, take home
your award!

Lesson 6

You know these consonants: א ב ה י מ ל פ פ ר שׁ ת תּ

You know these vowels: וֹ אֲ אַ אָ אֶ

NEW consonants: דּ
dalet
Sounds like **D**

ח
Chet
Sounds like **CH** (like clearing your throat)

NEW vowel: וּ
shuruk
Sounds like **U** in P<u>u</u>rim

READ WITH A TEACHER

REMEMBER: 1. We read Hebrew from RIGHT to LEFT.

2. Say the CONSONANT FIRST and the vowel second.

Right to Left Edition

THE HEBREW READER

Just for Kids

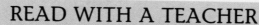

1   דּ דֶ דוֹ דִ דָּ דְ דֶל דוּ דְשׁ דוּב

2   חַ חוּ חֶ חָ חוֹ חִ חָר חֶה חוּת

3   לוּ בוּ מוּ יוּ הוּ דוּ פוּ שׁוּת מוּר

4   דִּי לוּת מוּשׁ חַב יֵשׁ פְּר הוֹד

Two syllables!

חַלָה
Challah

5   חַ-לָה חַלָה חַ-מָה חַמָה דַּ-מָה דָּמָה

6   שׁוּ-פָר שׁוֹפָר שׁוּ-פֵּר שׁוּפֵּר בְּ-פוּר בְּפוּר

7   דְּ-אוֹת דְּאוֹת אֶ-חוּד אֶחוּד אוֹ-פֵּד אוֹפֵד

8   שׁוּ-חֶת שׁוֹחֶת הִי-פוּר הִיפוּר חִי-דוּשׁ חִידוּשׁ

1 Practice writing. Write each consonant and vowel **six** times:

_____ _____ _____ _____ _____ _____

_____ _____ _____ _____ _____ _____

_____ _____ _____ _____ _____ _____

Write the word **three** times:

_____ _____ _____

דִּבּוּר

2 LOOK-ALIKE PAIRS: Some letters look alike. Check these out carefully.

ד
Dalet
Sounds like **D**

ר
Reish
Sounds like **R**

Circle every *dalet*. Put an X on every *reish*.

ד ר ר ד ז ד ר ו ז ר ד ך נ ר ד

ח
Chet
Sounds like **CH**

ה
Hei
Sounds like **H**

ת ת
Tav
Sounds like **T**

Circle every *CHet*. Put an X on every *hei*. Underline every *tav*:

ה ה ח ר ת ת ח ח ה ה ד ס ד ח ת ה

וֹ
Cholam
Sounds like OH in sh<u>o</u>far

וּ
Shuruk
Sounds like U in P<u>u</u>rim

Circle every *cholam*. Put an X on every *shuruk*:

וּ וּ ר ז וֹ ך ד וֹ ז וּ ז וֹ וּ ז וֹ ר

17

3 Letter review: Fill in the names and sounds of these consonants.

Lessons	א	ה	ד	ת	ל	שׁ	בּ
Name							
Sound							

Lessons	ר	ח	פ	מ	י	תּ
Name						
Sound						

4 Use your vowel ▊ and letter cards ▢ to make these syllables:

   a. Mah, Mee, Mu

   b. Lod, Lahd, Led

   c. Heer, Hur, Har

   d. Et, Ot, Ut (use the א)

   e. Shub, Shob, Sheeb

Answers for this lesson are on pages 76–77. When you finish this lesson, take home your award!

You know these consonants: א ב ד ה ח י פ ל מ ר שׁ תּ ת

You know these vowels: וֹ וּ אָ אַ אֶ אְ

NEW consonants: בּ ← *vet* Sounds like **V**

פּ ← *pei* Sounds like **P**

NEW vowel: אֵ ← *tzeirei* Sounds like **EI** in *Day**ei**nu*

Both ב and פ have sister letters. The only difference in how they look is the *dageish* (dot in the middle). The *dageish* changes the sound. Look:

בּ — ב

Sounds like: V B

פּ — פ

Sounds like: F P

On the next page, be careful when you read. Watch for the *dageish!*

19

Right to Left Edition

THE HEBREW READER

Just for Kids

1   בַּ בָּ בֶּ בֵּ בּוֹ   בּוּ בֶ בֹ בֵ בָ

2   פֹּו פֶ פָּ פֹּו פֹּו   פֶ פֶ פֶ פַ פֹּו

3   פּוּפ פֶּה פּוֹ דוֹפ   דְּפ רְפ הֶפ פָּר

4   בִּי בּוֹר בִּי הַב לֶבּ   לֵב בּוּם בּוּשׁ

Two syllables!

5   בָּ-בּוּם בָּבוּם בּוּ-מַף בּוּמַף פּוּ-מַף פּוּמַף

6   חֵ-פִּי חֵפִּי חֵי-פָּה חֵיפָּה חוּ-פָּה חוּפָּה

7   תּוּ-בָה תּוּבָה חוּ-בָה חוּבָה תּוּ-פֶּה תּוּפֶּה

8   אֶ-דוֹשׁ אֲדוֹשׁ אֵי-פוֹה אֵיפוֹה פֶּ-רוֹשׁ פֵּרוֹשׁ

9   לִי-מוּד לִימוּד דִּי-בּוּר דִּיבּוּר הַ-דוֹר הַדוֹר

10   פֶּ-לָא פֶּלָא יְ-לוֹהַ יְלוֹהַ הָ-לוֹא הָלוֹא

לוּלָב
Lulav

1 Practice writing. Write each consonant and vowel **six** times:

_____ _____ _____ _____ _____ _____

_____ _____ _____ _____ _____ _____

א א א א א א א

Write the word **three** times:

_____ _____ _____

פֵּרוּשׁ

2 Match the sounds:

1 Poh 2 Voh 3 Bee 4 Bu 5 Vu 6 Fu 7 Fei 8 Pei

_____ פֵּ   _____ בּוּ

_____ בוּ   _____ פֿוּ

_____ פֿוּ   _____ פֵ

_____ בוּ   _____ בְ

Answers for this lesson are on pages 78–79. When you finish this lesson, take home your award!

3 Circle the letter combinations in each line that sound the same:

a בִּימָה בְמָה בְּמַ בֶּמֶה בְּמַה בֶמָה

b חוּפָּה הוּפַ חוּפָה חוּפָּה תוּפַ חוּפָּא

c רְשֶׁת רֶשֶׁת דֶשֶׁת רֶשֶׁת רֶשֶׁח רָשֶׁת

d יוֹפָד יוּפָד יוּפָד יוּפָר יוֹפִיד יוּפִיד

You know these consonants: א ב ב ד ה ה ח י ל
מ פ פ שׁ ר ת ת

You know these vowels: אָ ו אִ אֵ אֶ אַ אָ

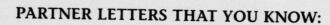

NEW consonants: ם ף   NEW vowel: אֻ

mem sofit
Sounds like **M**

fei sofit
Sounds like **F**

kubutz
Sounds like **U** in P<u>u</u>rim

Both of these new letters have the word *SOFIT* in their names. *SOFIT* MEANS "FINAL." These letters can only be used as the FINAL or LAST letter of a word. These letters have partner letters that are used at the beginning or in the middle of words.

PARTNER LETTERS THAT YOU KNOW:

מ = ם
mem = *mem sofit*
Sounds like **M**

פ = ף
fei = *fei sofit*
Sounds like **F**

READING RULE 4

Sofit letters can only appear at the **end of a word**. Their partner letters can only appear at the beginning or in the middle of a word.

22

Right to Left Edition

THE HEBREW READER

Just for Kids

1   אַף אוֹף פּוֹף לוֹף לֵף פֵּף תּוֹף תֹף

2   אֵם מֵם אוֹם חֵם חוֹם רָם פַּם מוּם

3   דְּ שֶׁ רְ מִ יְ בָּ בְ פָּ חָ בֵּ בְּ רְף

4   חֶשׁ חוּשׁ חֶשׁ שׁוּם שֵׁם פֶּה פוֹה פוּף פֵּף

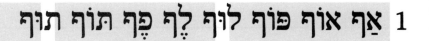

Two syllables!

5   אֶ-לֶף אָלֶף בִּי-שׁוֹר בִּישׁוֹר חָ-דֶר חֶדֶר

6   בֶּ-מָה בֶּמָה הֶ-לִי הֶלִי יֶ-דֶה יֶדֶה

7   פּוּ-חֵד פּוֹחֵד דָּ-לֶב דָּלֶב דָּ-לוּב דָּלוּב

8   תּוֹ-מֶם תּוֹמֶם תּוֹ-פֵּף תּוֹפֵּף יוּ-מֶף יוּמֶף

9   בֶּ-מָף בֶּמָף בּוּ-מֶם בּוּמֶם בּוּ-מֶם בּוּמֶם

10   הֶ-לֶשׁ הֶלֶשׁ הֶ-לוֹר הֶלוֹר חֶ-לוֹד חֶלוֹד

יְרוּשָׁלַיִם
Jerusalem

23   *Teacher's Signature* _____

1 Practice writing. Write each consonant and vowel **six** times:

_____ _____ _____ _____ _____ _____

_____ _____ _____ _____ _____ _____

א א א א א א א

Write the words **three** times.

_____ _____ _____

אַף

_____ _____ _____

פוּרִים

2 Remember: *Sofit* letters can only be at the **end of a word**. Their partner letters **can never be at the end of a word**. Fill in the blanks with the correct letters to spell these real words:

מ OR ם

Mem OR *Mem Sofit*

רוֹ_ָ	דָרוֹ_	בִּי_ָה	אֱ_ֶת	שָׁלוֹ_	_ַתִּיר
High place	South	Pulpit	Truth	Peace	Sets free

פ OR ף

Fei OR *Fei Sofit*

אַ_	אֶלֶ_	לָ_ֶא	יוֹ_ִי	חֵי_ָה	רוֹ_ֵא
Nose	Thousand	Wonders	Beauty	Haifa	Heals

24

3 Take out these letter cards:  ב ב ת ר מ י ם א ף פ פ ה

Take out these vowel cards: אָ אַ וּ אֶ אֵ אֲ אֱ אְָ

Use these cards to make these sound combinations.
(There might be more than one way!)

a. Ba-lam   b. Ei-ruv   c. Bu-maf   d. To-rah

e. Bee-pat   f. Tee-reif   g. Hu-mor   h. Mu-fah

Answers for this lesson are on pages 79–80. When you finish this lesson, take home your award!

25

Lesson 9

You know these consonants: א ב ג ד ה ח י ל מ ם פ פ ף ר ש ת ת

You know these vowels: ָ ֵ ֶ ִ ַ ֲ ֳ וּ וֹ

NEW consonants:

כ
CHaf
Sounds like **CH** (like
clearing your throat)

נ
nun
Sounds like **N**

צ
TZadi

READ WITH A TEACHER

REMEMBER: 1. We read Hebrew from RIGHT to LEFT. ⬅

2. Say the CONSONANT FIRST and the vowel second.

Right to Left Edition

THE HEBREW READER

Just for Kids

1 צָא צוֹ צוּ צֶה צִי צְ צָ צֶ צֵ

2 כֶה כֵּי כָ כוּ כָ כֶ כֵ כוֹ כַ כָ

3 נוּ נֵ נֶ נָא נִי נוֹ נֶ נָ נוּ

4 רוֹץ הֶן תֶּן כּוֹש לֶךְ כֶם צוֹד נֶץ

Two syllables AND MORE!

5 חָ-נוֹב חֲ-נוֹב מֵ-רוֹת אֲדוֹם אֱ-דוֹם

6 כִּבּוּש כִּי-בּוּש בִּיחוּש בִּי-חוּש פִּיהוּל פִּי-הוּל

7 הַלְלוּיָה הַלְ-לוּ-יָה הַלְלוּ הַ-לְ-לוּ הַלֵּל הַ-לֵל

8 דַיֵנוּ דַ-יֵ-נוּ הַמוֹצִיא הַ-מוֹ-צִיא הַמוֹ הַ-מוֹ

המוֹציא

בָּרוּךְ אַתָּה ה׳

Teacher's Signature _____

26

1 Practice writing. Write each consonant and vowel **six** times:

_____ _____ _____ _____ _____

_____ _____ _____ _____ _____

_____ _____ _____ _____ _____

Write the words **three** times.

_____ _____ _____ נֵצַח

_____ _____ _____ לָכֶם

2 *Vowel review!* Take out your *Alef Advancer* ▮. Read these syllables. Use your *Alef Advancer* to check yourself.

אָ   אוֹ   אָ   אֱ   אוֹ   אִ   אֵ   אַ

Now use your *Alef Advancer* to fill in the names of the vowels:

VOWEL: אֵ ַ _____   וֹ _____   אֱ _____   ָ _____

וֹ _____   אֱ _____   ַ _____   אִ _____

3 Circle the letters in each line that match the letter in the box:

a   פ   כ   ב   פ   כ   פ   ב   פ   כ   כ   כ   ב   פ   ב   ב   פ   **פ**

b   כ   ב   כ   ב   פ   כ   פ   ב   פ   כ   פ   ב   ב   ב   פ   **ב**

c   כ   ב   כ   פ   כ   פ   ב   כ   פ   כ   ב   פ   ב   ב   פ   **כ**

d   ר   ד   ה   ד   ר   ר   ך   ר   ו   ר   ד   ר   ח   ד   **ד**

4 Add the letter ב to these words.

Read the words with a friend.

מְ_וֹרָה   _ֵר   _ָבִיא   דַיֵ_וּ

Lamp   Candle   Prophet   Enough for us!

5 Draw line to match the words:

Pizza   צְדָקָה

Tzedakah   צִיצִת

HaMotzi   פִּיצָה

Beitzah   הַמוֹצִיא

Tzitzit   בֵּיצָה

Circle all of the letters that are *TZadi* צ in the words above.

Answers for this lesson are on pages 80–81. When you finish this lesson, take home your award!

28

You know these consonants:

מ ל כ י ח ה ד ב א

ת ת ש ר צ ק פ פ נ ס

You know these vowels:

וּ וֹ אֲ אַ אֶ אִ אֵ אָ אְ

NEW consonants:

ך	ן	ץ
CHaf sofit Sounds like **CH** (like clearing your throat)	*Nun sofit* Sounds like **N**	*TZadi sofit* Sounds like **TZ**

All the new letters are *SOFIT*, FINAL, letters. They can only be at the END of a word. All of the *SOFIT* letters have PARTNER letters that we use at the beginning or in the middle of a word.

All of the *SOFIT* letters and their PARTNERS are:

מ = ם   נ = ן   פ = ף

mem = mem sofit   *nun = nun sofit*   *fei = fei sofit*

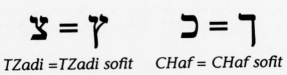

צ = ץ   כ = ך

TZadi =TZadi sofit   *CHaf = CHaf sofit*

Right to Left Edition

THE HEBREW READER

Just for Kids

1 אַךְ אֶךְ אַךְ אֵךְ רוּךְ דוּךְ דֶךְ דָךְ

2 אֶץ רֶץ שׁוּץ מוּץ בָּץ פָּץ נֶץ צֶץ

רַעֲשָׁן
noisemaker

3 פוֹן לוֹן נוּן נַן נֶן תָּן כֶן חֵן הֵן

4 לֵף לֶף יוֹן יָן יוֹם אָך שָׁך כוּף כֻם

Two syllables AND MORE!

5 מוּ-מֶם מוֹמֵם מוּ-מֶ-תִי מוֹמֶתִי נוּ-נְ-צִי נוֹנְצִי

6 בּוּ-יַת בּוּיַת פּוּ-יַת פּוּיַת הוּ-יְ-תוּ הוּיָתוּ

7 שֶׁ-בִים שֶׁבִים שֶׁ-פִּים שֶׁפִּים שֶׁ-בִי-לֵך שְׁבִילֵך

8 אָ-פֵּץ אָפֵּץ אָ-חוּץ אָחוּץ אָ-צֵה-חוּ אֲחוּצֵה

Real words!

9 אָ-לוֹ-הִים אֱלוֹהִים רְ-בּוֹן רִבּוֹן צוּ-רִי צוּרִי

10 בָּ-רוּך בָּרוּך כָּ-לָם כֻּלָם תּוֹ-רָ-ך תּוֹרָתֶך

1 Practice writing. Write each consonant and vowel **six** times:

_____ _____ _____ _____ _____ _____

_____ _____ _____ _____ _____ _____

_____ _____ _____ _____ _____ _____

Write the words **three** times.

_____ _____ _____ אָמֵן

_____ _____ _____ אֶרֶץ

2 Fill in the blanks with the correct letters to spell these real words:

Remember: *Sofit* letters can only be at the **end of a word**.
Their partner letters **can never be at the end of a word**.

נ or ן
Nun or Nun Sofit

מִפִּי_וּ   רַחֲמָ_   _צָח   בָּ_ִים   _בִיא   צִיוֹ_

כ or ך
CHaf or CHaf Sofit

_מוֹ_ה   מֶלֶ_   בְּ_ל   דֶּרֶ_   אֶתְ_ם   בָּרוּ_

צ or ץ
TZadi or TZadi Sofit

רָ_וֹן   אוֹמֶ_   _וּר   אֶרֶ_   מִ_ְרַיִם   _יוֹן

3 Draw lines connecting the letters to their partners:

ץ   ם   ן   ף   ך

מ   צ   כ   פ   נ

Answers for this lesson are on pages 81–82. When you finish this lesson, take home your award!

You know these consonants: א ב ג ד ה ח ט י כ ך ל מ ם
נ ן פ ף ף צ ץ ר שׁ ת ת

You know these vowels: וּ וֹ אָ אֶ אֵ אִ אֱ אֹ

NEW consonants:

כ
kaf
Sounds like **K**

ק
kuf
Sounds like **K**

NEW vowel: אְ
sh'va

Sounds either:

1. like a **pause** (') at the **beginning** of a syllable, as in *b'rachah* or *Sh'ma*.

2. **silent** (-) at the **end** of a syllable, as in *Yis-rael* or *Av-raham*.

READING RULE 5

All letters in a word **must have a vowel.**

Exceptions to this rule:

1. The last letter of a word doesn't have to have a vowel.

2. The letters א and י can be in the middle of a word without a vowel.

33

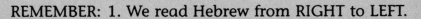

Right to Left Edition

THE HEBREW READER

Just for Kids

צְדָקָה
Tzedakah

1　כָּ כּוֹ כִּי כַּה כֶּא כָה כֶּ כֶה כּוּ כָּ כְּ

2　קוֹ קָן קֶה קַ קְ קֶן קוֹ קֶן קוּ קַ קוֹק קָף

3　כֶם כּוּם קָם כָּן כֵּן תֶּק רוּכ דַּק כִּיש

Two syllables AND MORE:
REMEMBER: At the **beginning** of a syllable *sh'va* ְ
sounds like a **pause** ('), as in *b'rachah* or *Sh'ma.*

4　כְּ-לָה כְּלָה קְ-פְּ-לָה קְפְלֶה שְׁ-בּוּ-כִי שְׁבוּכִי

5　מְ-קוּף מְקוּף כְּ-בֵּץ כְּבֵּץ כְּ-בּוּ-צִין כְּבּוּצִין

REMEMBER: At the **end** of a syllable *sh'va* ְ
sounds **silent** (-), as in *Yis-rael* or *Av-raham.*

6　יִשְׁ-אָה יִשְׁאָה מִכְ-פָּה מִכְפָּה מִקְ-צֶה מִקְצֶה

7　אֶבְ-יֵן אֶבְיֵן הֶנְ-קֶף הֶנְקֶף יַנְ-אִי-כּוּ יַנְאִיכּוּ

Real words!

8　נִשְׁ-מַת נִשְׁמַת נִשְׁ-מַ-תִי נִשְׁמַתִי נִקְ-רָא נִקְרָא

9　בְּ-כָ-בוֹד בְּכְבוֹד לְ-דוּ-דִי לְדוֹדִי יְ-הִי יְהִי

10　לְ-בָבְ-ךָ לְבָבְךָ יְ-רוּ-שָׁה יְרוּשָׁה
　　יְ-רוּ-שָׁ-לַ-יִם יְרוּשָׁלַיִם

Teacher's Signature _____

1 Practice writing. Write each consonant and vowel **six** times:

_____ _____ _____ _____ _____ _____

_____ _____ _____ _____ _____ _____

⅄ ⅄ ⅄ ⅄ ⅄ ⅄ אָ

Write the word **three** times:

_____ _____ _____ כִּפָּה

_____ _____ _____ קְלָף

2 Circle the letters in each line that sound like K.

כ ב מ פּ כ כ כ פ ב כ נ נ כ כ כ a

ד ק פּ ל ק ד ֽצ ק כ ד פ ל ד ק b

ק ב ד כ כ ק ח פּ כ פ ק כ ן ב ק c

3 Match the words to the pictures:

צְדָקָה

חֲנֻכָּה

כִּפָּה

אֲפִיקוֹמָן

פְּרִי

4 Fill in the *SH'VA* vowel wherever it is needed. Use Reading Rule 5 at the bottom of page 36 to complete this activity.

פְּרִי	צִיצִית	בְּרָכָה	יִצְחָק
Fruit	Fringes	Blessing	Isaac

בְּרֵאשִׁית	תְּפִילָה	קְלָף	צֵאתְכֶם
Beginning	Prayer	Parchment	Your going out

5 THE SOUND OF THE VOWEL SH'VA אְ

A *sh'va* at the BEGINNING of a syllable makes a **pause**.

Examples: מְנוֹרָה לְחַיִּים

A *sh'va* at the END of a syllable is silent.

Examples: הַבְדָּלָה אַבְרָהָם

READD THE WORDS BELOW:

⭐ Put a circle around each *sh'va* that is a **pause**.

⭐ Put an X on each *sh'va* that is **silent**.

For example: מְנוֹרָה הַבְדָּלָה אַבְרָהָם לְחַיִּים

קְהִילָה יְרוּשָׁלַיִם מַלְכוּת תְּפִילָה לִפְנֵי נִקְרָא

בְּצִיּוֹן לְכָה בְּמָקוֹם לְבָבְךָ מִצְרַיִם פְּרִי

Answers for this lesson are on pages 82–83. When you finish this lesson, take home your award!

You know these consonants: א ב ב ד ה ה ח י כ כ ך ל מ ם
נ ן פ פ ף צ ץ ק ר ש ת ת

You know these vowels: וּ וֹ אָ אֵ אֶ אִ אֱ אָ

There are *six* groups of letters that we can call **families**. The family groups are:

ב ב	כ כ ך	מ ם	נ ן
פ פ ף	צ ץ		

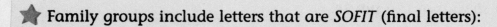

⭐ Family groups include letters that are *SOFIT* (final letters):

צ = ץ   פ = ף   נ = ן   מ = ם   כ = ך

⭐ Family groups include letters that look exactly the same except that one of them has a *dageish* (dot in the middle). The *dageish* **changes the sound** of the letter:

ב - ב   כ - כ   פ - פ

⭐ Two family groups include letters with a *dageish* AND *sofit* letters:

כ - כ - ך   פ - פ - ף

READING RULE 6

Letters in the same "family" can take each other's places. They are the same letter in different forms.

Right to Left Edition

THE HEBREW READER

Just for Kids

1   כֵּן בֵּן בְּנֶ בֵּב כְּב כָּב כְּבְ כְּם כְּמ

2   בּוּף פּוּף פּוּץ בּוּצ בּוּ נַךְ נַךְ נַן

3   אוֹץ אַף אַפְ אַף אֶץ אֶן אֶכְ אֶךְ

קְלָף
Mezuzah scroll

4   צָדְי צָ-דְי פֵּי פֵּי כָּף כַּף מֶם נוּן

Two syllables AND MORE!

5   רְכָךְ רְ-כָךְ רְכָה רִ-כָה לְבָה לְ-בָה

6   חֶצְיוֹנֶת חֶצְ-יוֹ-נֶת חֶצְיוֹן חֶצְ-יוֹן חֵץ

7   דִבְיוֹק דִבְ-יוֹק דֵבְפִּים דֵבְ-פִּים דֵבּוּף דֵ-בּוּף

8   בִּפְהֵיצוּת בִּפְהֵי-צוּת בִּפְהֶץ בִּפְ-הֶץ פַּהֶץ פַּ-הֶץ

Real words!

9   מְבָרֵךְ מְ-בָ-רֵךְ בָּרוּךְ בָּ-רוּךְ בָּרְכוּ בָּ-רְ-כוּ

10   צִיוֹנוּת צְ-יוֹ-נוּת קְלָפִים קְלָ-פִּים קֶלֶף קֶלֶף

Teacher's Signature _____

39

1 Practice writing. Write the words **three** times:

קִבּוּץ

_____ _____ _____

מְבוֹרָךְ

_____ _____ _____

צִיוֹן

_____ _____ _____

פוּרִים

_____ _____ _____

2 Take out these *Alef-bet Letter Cards*: ⬛

ץ פּ ס ן מ צ ף כ נ ך כּ בּ פ בּ כ

a Organize them into their family groups.

b Do you know all of their names. Use your *Alef-bet Chart* or your *Alef Advancer* ⬛ letter strips to check your answers.

c Take out all of the *SOFIT* letters. There are five. Match them to their partner letters that appear in the middle or beginning of a word.

3 Circle the letter combinations in each line that have the SAME SOUND:

a בָּרוּן כָדוֹן כַּדוֹנ קַדוּן קָרוּן כָדוֹן בָּדוּם

b פְּבֵּצ פְּבֵּצ פִּיבֵּף פְּבֵּף פִּיבֵּץ פִּיבֵּךְ מִיבֵּץ

c בּוּכֶם כּוּבֵם כְּבֵם בּוּבֵם בּוּבֵם כְּפֵּם כּוּבֶם

Answers for this lesson are on pages 83–84. When you finish this lesson, take home your award!

40

Lesson 13

You know these consonants: א ב ב ד ה ה ח י כ כ ך ל מ ם
נ ן פ פ ף צ ץ ק ר ש ת ת

You know these vowels: ְ ֱ ֵ ִ ַ ָ ֶ ו וֹ

NEW consonants:

ט
tet
Sounds like **T**

ע
ayin
Sound is *silent*

ג
gimel
Sounds like **G**

NEW vowel:

X

cholam chaseir
Sounds like **O** in
*shal**o**m*

READ WITH A TEACHER

REMEMBER: 1. We read Hebrew from RIGHT to LEFT. ⬅

2. Say the CONSONANT FIRST and the vowel second.

THE HEBREW READER

Just for Kids

1   עָר עוֹד עוֹב עֵל עֶם עֵ עָל עֵ

2   גֵית גַּג גְּכ גַּ גָן גֵץ גֵּשׁ גוֹ גֵ

3   טָב טֹק טֹ טוֹ טֵב טוֹנ טַם טֶת טֵ

4   עֵג גֵע חֹט תֹל פֹּף כֹּר מֹ בֹ לֹ

Continued on next page

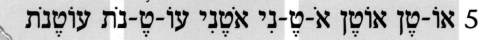

Two syllables AND MORE!

5 אוֹ-טֶן אוֹטֶן אֹ-טֶ-נִי אֹטֶנִי עוֹ-טֶ-נִי עוֹ-טֶ-נֹת עוֹטֶנֹת

6 טְ-גֶע טְגֶע עֶגְ-טֶע עֶגְטֶת עֶגְ-מֶת עֶגְמֶת

7 צָ-פֹוא צָפֹוא עָ-פֹא עָפֹא צָ-פֹ-אִין צָפֹאִין

אֶתְרוֹג
Etrog

8 נְ-בוּ-אָה נְבוּאָה גְ-בְ-עָה גְבְעָה נְ-גְ-נָה נְגְנָה

Real words!

9 עוֹ-לָם עוֹלָם עוֹ-לָ-מִים עוֹלָמִים בָּ-עוֹ-לָם בָּעוֹלָם

10 אֶתְ-רוֹג אֶתְרוֹג אֱ-לֹ-הֵי אֱלֹהֵי אֱ-לֹ-הֵי-נוּ אֱלֹהֵינוּ

Teacher's Signature _____

On Your Own

1 Practice writing. Write each consonant and vowel **six** times:

_____ _____ _____ _____ _____ _____

_____ _____ _____ _____ _____ _____

_____ _____ _____ _____ _____ _____

Write the word **three** times:

גִבּוֹר

_____ _____ _____

טַלִית

_____ _____ _____

2 Circle all the letters in each line that match the sound of the English letter:

WATCH OUT!	ט looks like מ	ע looks like צ
	tet *mem*	*ayin* *TZadi*

ג looks like נ
gimel   *nun*

Sounds like T   ת ט ד ת כ ט ת שׁ ת ט צ ט

Sounds like T   ט מ ב ט ע שׁ ט מ ס ט פ ט

Sounds silent   א ח ע ע ך א מ ע ץ ר א ע

Sounds silent   ע ג צ ע ץ פ ע א צ ע ע מ

Sounds like G   ד ג ה נ ג כ ג נ ת י ג ן

3 Match the syllables that sound the same.
Write the number in the blank:

___תְּגָא	תוֹם 1
___כְּרוֹם	עוֹד 2
___מֹנֶע	טָגֶה 3
___רְעוֹת	מוֹנֶה 4
___אֶד	קֶרֹמ 5
___טֹמ	רַאְט 6

Answers for this lesson are on page 84. When you finish this lesson, take home your award!

43

You know these consonants: א ב ב ג ד ה ה ח ט י כ כ ך ל מ
ם נ ן פ פ ף ע צ ץ ק ר שׁ ת ת

You know these vowels: וֹ וּ אֹ אָ אֶ אֵ אֶ אֵ אִ אָ אַ

NEW consonants:

שׂ
sin
Sounds like **S**

ס
samech
Sounds like **S**

ז
zayin
Sounds like **Z**

Both **שׂ** and **ס** sound like S. Be careful—they both look like other letters that you know:

שׂ looks like **שׁ**
Sin   SHin

ס looks like **ם**
Samech   Mem *sofit*

READ WITH A TEACHER

REMEMBER: 1. We read Hebrew from RIGHT to LEFT.

2. Say the CONSONANT FIRST and the vowel second.

Right to Left Edition

THE HEBREW READER

Just for Kids

1   שֶׁ שָׁ שְׁ שׂוֹ שׁוּ שָׁ שֶׁ שְׁ שִׁי שֵׁ שֶׁה שֶׁ

2   סָ סוּ סֶ סוֹ ס סְא סֶם שֶׁם שֶׁם שֶׁ

3   זוֹ זָ זֶ זֵ זֶע זִ זִי זָם זְ זֵם זֹס זוּשׁ

4   עוֹז עַם אִיס אֵם שְׂא סַז שׁוּח חֶט

44

Two syllables AND MORE!

מְזוּזָה
Mezuzah

5 עֵ-זוֹ עִזּוֹ צֵ-עִיד צְעִיד זֵבְ-רוֹן זֶבְרוֹן

6 שְׂ-אוּ שְׂאוּ יְשְׂ-יֶשׁ יְשִׁישׁ שֵׂ-סוּךְ שֵׂסוּךְ

7 חָ-טִיס חָטִיס חָ-מִים חָמִים סֵ-פֶּר סֵפֶּר

8 זְ-רוּ זְרוּ זְ-פֶּ-נוּ זְפֶּנוּ דִי-זִי דִיזִי

9 אֶבְ-שׁוֹן אֶבְשׁוֹן הַגְ-יֵ-קָם הַגְיֵקָם נְ-קָס נְקָס

10 לְ-צָ-פוּז לְצָפוּז לְ-עָ-מִים לְעָמִים בְּ-חָ-סֶד בְּחֶסֶד

Real words!

11 מְ-זוּ-זָה מְזוּזָה יִשְׂ-רָ-אֵל יִשְׂרָאֵל סֻ-כּוֹת סֻכּוֹת

12 נֹא-מַר נֹאמַר כֹּ-הֵן כֹּהֵן מְ-בָ-רֵךְ מְבֹרָךְ

13 זִ-כָּ-רוֹן זִכָּרוֹן כַּרְ-פַּס כַּרְפַּס שְׂמְ-חַת שִׂמְחַת

Teacher's Signature _____

1 Practice writing. Write each consonant and vowel **six** times:

Exercise **1** continued on next page

45

1 (continued)

Write the word **three** times:

מְזוּזָה

_____ _____ _____

חֶסֶד

_____ _____ _____

2 You know all of the vowels on your *Alef Advancer* ▢ strip! Use your *Alef Advancer* to review the names and sounds of the vowels. Then fill in this chart:

Name	patach	kamatz	shuruk	sh'va	segol	kubutz	cholam	tzeirei	chirik	cholam chaseir
Looks like										
Sounds like										

3 Circle the letters in each line that have the same sound as the English letter:

S   שׁ שׁ שׂ ס ט שׂ ם ס ת פ ס ס שׁ שׁ ם שׁ שׂ שׁ

Z   ס י ז שׁ ד ו ז ץ ז ס ר ז ו צ ז ו

TZ   ן צ פ ץ צ שׁ ז ע שׂ צ ע ז ס ץ צ ן

Answers for this lesson are on page 84. When you finish this lesson, take home your award!

Lesson 15

You know these consonants:
א ב ג ד ה ז ח ט י כ ך ל מ ם
נ ן ס ע פ ף צ ק ר שׁ תּ ת

You know these vowels: וּ וֹ אֹ אָ אֶ אֵ אִ אַ אְ

Remember:

READING RULE 5

All letters in a word **must have a vowel.**

Exceptions to this rule:

1. The last letter of a word doesn't have to have a vowel.

2. The letters א and י can be in the middle of a word without a vowel.

New Rule:

READING RULE 7

The dot above a שׁ or שׂ can be a "double-duty dot."

Sometimes it serves as the dot for the letter AND a cholam chaseir vowel (אֹ).

Examples:

נָשׂוֹא→נָשֹׂא   מוֹשֶׁה→מֹשֶׁה

47

Right to Left Edition

THE HEBREW READER

Just for Kids

Two syllables AND MORE!

1 שׁוֹ-לָה שׁוֹלָה שׁ-לָה שָׁלָה אֶ-שֹׁר אשׁר

2 פֶּ-דוֹשׁ פֵּדוֹשׁ פֶּ-דֹשׁ פֵּדֹשׁ חָ-תֹשׁ חְתֹשׁ

3 כֹּ-שָׁן כֹּשָׁן שֹׁבְ-טֶ-נֵת שֹׁבְטֶנֶת מָ-שֹׁךְ מָשֹׁךְ

4 בֹּ-שֶׁק בֹּשֶׁק זֶ-עֹשׁ זְעֹשׁ שֹׁ-סָא שֹׁסָא

משֶׁה

Real words!

5 מֹ-שֶׁה מֹשֶׁה חֹ-שֶׁךְ חֹשֶׁךְ רֹאשׁ רֹאשׁוֹ

6 שָׁ-לֹשׁ שָׁלֹשׁ נֹ-חֹ-שֶׁת נְחֹשֶׁת קָ-דוֹשׁ קָדוֹשׁ

7 יֶ-חֶ-שֹׂף יֶחֶשֹׂף עָ-שֹׂה עָשֹׂה שָׂ-שֹׂן שָׂשֹׂן

8 שֹׂנְ-אֵי שֹׂנְאֵי לִפְ-רֹשׁ לִפְרֹשׁ שָׂ-מֵ-חִים שְׂמֵחִים

Teacher's Signature _____

Answers for this lesson are on page 85. When you finish this lesson, take home your award!

On Your Own

1 Circle all the letters that are שׁ. Underline all the letters that are שׂ.

שְׁלֹשֶׁת שָׂרָה קָדוֹשׁ יֶחֶשֹׂף עֹשֶׂה

יִשְׂרָאֵל יְטֹשׁ יֹשְׁבֵי שָׁשֹׁן שׁוֹפָר

2 Circle the dots that are "double-duty dots." (These dots are BOTH a *cholam chaseir* vowel AND the dot for the letters שׂ or שׁ.)

קָדוֹשׁ שָׁשֹׁן רֹאשׁ יֶחֶשֹׂף שִׂמְחָה

לִפְרֹשׁ נְחֹשֶׁת נָשָׂא שִׂמוּשׁ לִפְרֹושׁ

48

Lesson 16

You know these consonants:

אבבגדהזחטיכךלמם
ןנסעפפףצץקרששתת

You know these vowels: וֹ וּ אֹ אַ אֲ אִ אֵ אֶ

NEW consonant: ו
vav
Sounds like **V**

PAY ATTENTION!
The consonant ו looks very much like the vowels וֹ and וּ.

This rule will help you tell if ו is being used as a consonant or a vowel.

READING RULE 8

Each consonant can have only one vowel.

Right to Left Edition

THE HEBREW READER

Just for Kids

1   וֹ וָ וְ וִ וּ וֹ וֹ וָ וְ וַ וִ וֵא

2   וָוּ ווֹה תָיו אֹב אוֹ וֶק רֶק וְים

Two syllables AND MORE!

3   וָ-בוּם וָבוּם יוֹ-לִי-חוּ יוֹלִיחוּ יוֹ-לִי-חַיו יוֹלְיחָיו

4   רְ-דוֹשׁ רְדוֹשׁ גֶ-דוֹוּ גְדוֹוּ נָ-דְיו נָדְיו

5   תֶ-מָיו תֶמָיו תֶּ-טָיו תֶּטָיו תֶּ-טָ-ווֹת תֶּטָווֹת

6   בְּ-וו בְּוו בְּ-וֹק בְּוֹק בְּ-וֹ-כִּיר בּוֹכִּיר

Real words!

7   לְ-עוֹ-לָם לְעוֹלָם עוֹ-לְ-מוֹ עוֹלְמוֹ עוֹ-לְ-מָיו עוֹלָמָיו

8   מִצְ-וָה מִצְוָה מִצְ-ווֹת מִצְווֹת בְּ-מִצְ-וֹ-תָיו בְּמִצְוֹתָיו

9   וָ-עֶד וָעֶד וְ-אַ-הַב-תָּ וְאַהַבְתָּ בְּמְ-רוֹ-מָיו בְּמְרוֹמָיו

Real Prayers!

דָּוִד
David

10   עֹשֶׂה שָׁלוֹם בִּמְרוֹמָיו הוּא יַעֲשֶׂה שָׁלוֹם

11   אֲשֶׁר קִדְּשָׁנוּ בְּמִצְוֹתָיו וְצִוָּנוּ

12   לְהַדְלִיק נֵר שֶׁל שַׁבָּת

13   דָּוִד מֶלֶךְ יִשְׂרָאֵל

1 Practice writing. Write each consonant and vowel **six** times:

1
ן
2

_____ _____ _____ _____ _____ _____

Write the words **three** times:

וְצִוָּנוּ

_____ _____ _____

וָעֶד

_____ _____ _____

2 Circle all the letters that sound like V.

וּ וְ בֵ יַ בַּ וּ כֵ וֹ וֹ בַ וּ

וּ ןְ וֹ זַ דֵ וֹ רַ וֹ זַ ךֵ וָ זַ ז

3 In the words below:

Circle the **וּ**s that are CONSONANTS. Underline the **וּ**s that are VOWELS.

a צוּרִי מִצְוָה מִצְוֹת בְּמִצְוֹתָיו בִּמְרוֹמָיו

b צִיּוֹן צִיּוֹנוּת וְצִוָּנוּ וְהֶגְיוֹן וְאָהַבְתָּ

c דוֹד דָּוִד דּוֹר דּוֹרָיו לְעוֹלָם וָעֶד

4 Take out your *Alef-bet Letter Cards* ☐.
YOU KNOW ALL OF THE HEBREW
CONSONANTS NOW! Go through your letter
cards to test your knowledge of each letter's
name and sound. Check yourself with your
Alef-bet Letter Chart or your *Alef Advancer* ☐.
You can do this with a friend!

Answers for
this lesson are on
page 86. When you
finish this lesson, take
home your award!

5 Use your *Alef-bet Letter Chart* to help you put
all of the consonants in alphabetical order.

Lesson 17

You know these consonants:

א ב ב ג ד ה ו ז ח ט י כ כ ך ל מ ם
נ ן ס ע פ פ ף צ ץ ק ר ש שׂ ת ת

You know these vowels: אֹ אֶ אֵ אִ אַ אָ אְ וּ

NEW vowel SOUNDS: These are all vowels that you already know. They have different sounds in these special combinations!

אַי sounds like **AY** in *dayeinu*

אָי sounds like **AY** in *dayeinu*

וֹי sounds like **OY** in *Oy vey!*

וּי sounds like **UEY** in chop *suey*

READ WITH A TEACHER

REMEMBER: 1. We read Hebrew from RIGHT to LEFT.

2. Say the CONSONANT FIRST and the vowel second.

1 אַי פַּי פֵּי יֵי נַי חַי כֵּי רֵי דִי

2 לֵי לֵין דַיִץ רָים מֵים סִין הָי תָי

3 אוֹי עוֹי קוֹי בּוֹי ווֹי זוֹי שׁוֹי טוֹי פּוֹי

לַיְלָה

4 גוּי נוּי סוּי שׁוּי לוּי עוּי צוּי חוּי מוּי

Real words!

5 דַי-יֵ-נוּ דַיֵּינוּ לַי-לָה לַיְלָה אַ-דֹ-נָי אֲדֹנָי

6 אוֹ-יֵב אוֹיֵב גוֹי גוֹי-יִם גּוֹיִים רָ-אוּי רָאוּי

7 אֱ-לֹ-הַי אֱלֹהַי גְּ-לוּי גָּלוּי לְ-חַ-יִם לְחַיִים

52

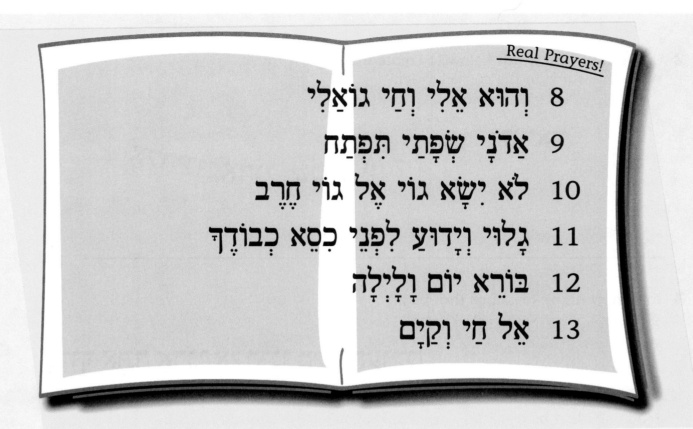

8 וְהוּא אֵלִי וְחַי גּוֹאֲלִי

9 אֲדֹנָי שְׂפָתַי תִּפְתָּח

10 לֹא יִשָּׂא גוֹי אֶל גּוֹי חֶרֶב

11 גָּלוּי וְיָדוּעַ לִפְנֵי כִסֵּא כְבוֹדֶךָ

12 בּוֹרֵא יוֹם וָלָיְלָה

13 אֵל חַי וְקַיָּם

Teacher's Signature _____

On Your Own

1 ON YOUR OWN

Circle the sound combinations and words that rhyme in each line.

a	שְׂפָתַי	לְפָנַי	לְפָנָיו	שְׁבִיעִי	נְבִיאֵי
b	גָּלוּ	גָּלוּי	מַשּׂוּי	שָׁמוֹ	שְׁמִי
c	אוֹיֵב	סָאוּ	סְעוּי	וְגוּי	וְגוֹי
d	אֲבוֹתַי	לְחַיִּים	מִצְוֺתַי	עֲשׂוּי	אוֹי

53

2 Unscramble the words below to create the שְׁמַע prayer.
Write the words in the correct order.

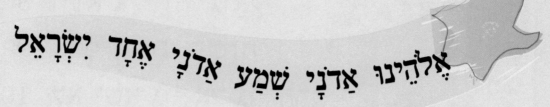

אֱלֹהֵינוּ אֲדֹנָי שְׁמַע אֲדֹנָי אֶחָד יִשְׂרָאֵל

_____

3 You know many blessings that begin

בָּרוּךְ אַתָּה אֲדֹנָי אֱלֹהֵינוּ מֶלֶךְ הָעוֹלָם

Read each line below. There are TWO mistakes in each line. Circle them:

a בָּרוּךְ אֶתָּה אֲדֹנָי אֱלֹהֵינוּ טֶלֶךְ הָעוֹלָם

b בָּרוּךְ אֲדֹנָי אַתָּה אֱלֹהֵינוּ מֶלֶךְ הָעוֹלְם

c בָּרוּךְ אַתָּה אֲדֹנָי אֱלֹהֵינוּ מֶלֶךְ הָעוֹלָם

d בָּרוּךְ אַתָּה אֲדֹנָי אֱלֹהֵינוּ מֶלֶךְ הַצוֹלָם

Answers for this lesson are on pages 86–87. When you finish this lesson, take home your award!

54

Lesson 18

You know these consonants: א ב ב ג ד ה ו ז ח ט י כ ך ל מ ם
נ ן ס ע פ פ ף צ ץ ק ר שׁ שׂ ת ת

You know these vowels: אֹ ו וֹ אֲ אָ אַ אֶ אֵ אְ אִ

You know these vowel sounds: אַי אָי אוּי אוֹי

The Jewish people commonly call God *Adonai* אֲדֹנָי. This word means "my Lord." God's actual name is a secret that no one knows! In the Torah, God's name is written as יְהֹוָה or יְיָ. In ancient days the כֹּהֵן גָּדוֹל, the High Priest of the Holy Temple, knew how to pronounce God's name. Even he was only allowed to say it out loud once a year, on Yom Kippur. The name of God is very special and very holy.

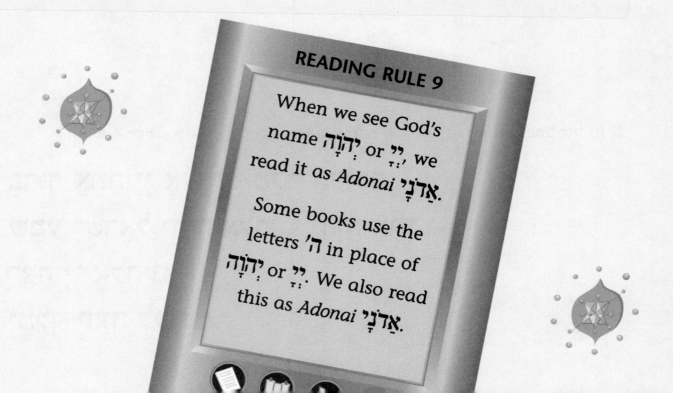

READING RULE 9

When we see God's name יְיָ or יְהֹוָה, we read it as *Adonai* אֲדֹנָי.

Some books use the letters ה׳ in place of יְיָ or יְהֹוָה. We also read this as *Adonai* אֲדֹנָי.

READ WITH A TEACHER

Read these phrases from prayers

<u>Real Prayers!</u>

1 אַתָּה גִבּוֹר לְעוֹלָם אֲדֹנָי

2 קָדוֹשׁ קָדוֹשׁ קָדוֹשׁ יְהֹוָה צְבָאוֹת

3 אֱ-לֹ-הֵי-כֶם אֱלֹהֵיכֶם, אֲנִי יְהֹוָה אֱלֹהֵיכֶם

4 יְיָ אֱלֹהַי וֵאלֹהֵי אֲבוֹתַי

5 מִי כָמֹכָה בָּאֵלִים יְהֹוָה

6 יְהֹוָה יִמְלֹךְ לְעוֹלָם וָעֶד

Teacher's Signature _____

1 In the lines below, circle each name of God that we **pronounce** *Adonai*.

a בָּרוּךְ אַתָּה יְיָ אֱלֹהֵינוּ מֶלֶךְ הָעוֹלָם

b שְׁמַע יִשְׂרָאֵל יְהֹוָה אֱלֹהֵינוּ יְהֹוָה אֶחָד

c רְצֵה יְיָ אֱלֹהֵינוּ

d יִמְלֹךְ יְהֹוָה לְעוֹלָם

56

2 The תּוֹרָה and סִדּוּר (prayer book) use many names and descriptions for God. Below is a list of some of these names with their meanings. Read the names in Hebrew with a friend. If you don't agree on how to say a word, ask for help. Pay attention to what the meaning of the word is.

d מֶ-לֶךְ מֶלֶךְ = King

a הָ-מְ-רַ-חֵם הַמְרַחֵם = Compassionate One

e הַ-גִ-בּוֹר הַגִּבּוֹר = The Mighty

b אֵל עֶל-יוֹן אֵל עֶלְיוֹן = God on High

f בּוֹ-רֵא בּוֹרֵא = Creator

c צוּר יִשְׂ-רָ-אֵל צוּר יִשְׂרָאֵל = Rock Israel

3 Each of God's names above describes a different quality of God. Fill in the blanks below with ideas about God.

EXAMPLES:

When I call God הַגִּבּוֹר *I think God can accomplish anything.*

When I call God עֶלְיוֹן *I imagine God in the vastness of the sky.*

YOUR TURN:

When I call God מֶלֶךְ *I* _____

When I call God בּוֹרֵא *I* _____

When I call God צוּר יִשְׂרָאֵל *I* _____

When I call God הַמְרַחֵם *I* _____

Answers for this lesson are on page 87. When you finish this lesson, take home your award!

You know these consonants:

אבבגדהוזחטיככךלמם
ןנסעפפףצץקרששתת

You know these vowels: אֹ אָ אַ אֶ אֵ אִ וּ וֹ

You know these vowel sounds: אַי אָי אוֹי אֹי

 **This lesson is about dots and other marks that do not change the sounds we read.**

1 You know these pairs of "sister" letters. Write their names and sounds below them:

פ - פּ	כ - כּ	ב - בּ

Sound	F – P	ch – K	V – B
Name	feiⅇ – Pey	chaf – Kaf	Vet – Bet

These "sister" letters sometimes take each other's places in different forms of the same word. They are considered to be like the same letter. **But** the דָּגֵשׁ (dot) inside these letters changes the sound.

Sometimes a דָּגֵשׁ will show up in other letters. Some examples are:

ק מ ז ס
שׁ ט ד ל

When that happens, **the sound does not change**. The דָּגֵשׁ is important for grammar reasons that you will learn as you continue to study Hebrew. For now, just remember this rule:

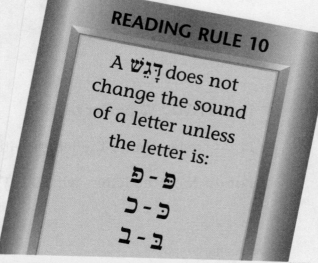

2 The *meteg* מֶתֶג is a Hebrew accent mark. It looks like this under a letter: אָ.

The מֶתֶג does not change the sound of a letter or the vowel under it. The מֶתֶג helps the reader know where to put the accent on the word.

READ WITH A TEACHER

Read these words and phrases from prayers:

Real Words!

1 נְ-קַ-דֵּשׁ נְקַדֵּשׁ כָּ-לָ-נוּ כֻּלָּנוּ עַ-מֶ-ךָ עַמֶּךָ הַ-טּוֹב הַטּוֹב

2 עָ-לֵי-נוּ עָלֵינוּ קִ-וִּי-נוּ קִוִּינוּ רָ-צִי-תָ רָצִיתָ נַ-גִּיד נַגִּיד

3 הַ-קָ-דוֹשׁ הַקָּדוֹשׁ וְ-יִשְׁ-תַּ-בַּח וְיִשְׁתַּבַּח

4 מַל-כוּ-תֶ-ךָ מַלְכוּתֶךָ עֻ-זֶ-ךָ עֻזֶּךָ וְ-יִ-פְּ-לוּ וְיִפְּלוּ

5 מִי כָמֹכָה נֶאְדָּר בַּקֹּדֶשׁ

6 אֲשֶׁר קִדְּשָׁנוּ בְּמִצְוֹתָיו וְצִוָּנוּ

7 אֶשָּׂא עֵינַי אֶל הֶהָרִים

8 דָּוִד מֶלֶךְ יִשְׂרָאֵל חַי וְקַיָּם

Teacher's Signature _____

1 In the מִי כָמֹכָה prayer below:

⭐ Put a circle around the letters with a דָּגֵשׁ if the sound changes.

⭐ Put an X on the letters with a דָּגֵשׁ if the sound **does not change**.

מִי־כָמֹכָה בָּאֵלִים, יְיָ?

מִי כָּמֹכָה, נֶאְדָּר בַּקֹּדֶשׁ,

נוֹרָא תְהִלֹּת, עֹשֵׂה פֶלֶא?

שִׁירָה חֲדָשָׁה שִׁבְּחוּ גְאוּלִים לְשִׁמְךָ עַל־שְׂפַת הַיָּם; יַחַד כֻּלָּם

הוֹדוּ וְהִמְלִיכוּ וְאָמְרוּ: "יְיָ יִמְלֹךְ לְעוֹלָם וָעֶד!"

2 Circle any מֶתֶג that you find in the מִי כָמֹכָה prayer below.

מִי־כָמֹכָה בָּאֵלִים, יְיָ?

מִי כָּמֹכָה, נֶאְדָּר בַּקֹּדֶשׁ,

נוֹרָא תְהִלֹּת, עֹשֵׂה פֶלֶא?

שִׁירָה חֲדָשָׁה שִׁבְּחוּ גְאוּלִים לְשִׁמְךָ עַל־שְׂפַת הַיָּם; יַחַד כֻּלָּם

הוֹדוּ וְהִמְלִיכוּ וְאָמְרוּ: "יְיָ יִמְלֹךְ לְעוֹלָם וָעֶד!"

What does the מֶתֶג do to the way we read the word?

_____

Answers for
this lesson are on
page 88. When you
finish this lesson, take
home your award!

60

You know these consonants: אבבגדההוזחטיככךלמם
נןסעפפףצץקרששתת

You know these vowels: וֹ אָ אֶ אֱ אֲ אַ אֵ אִ אֻ

You know these vowel sounds: אַי אָי אוִי אוֹי

This lesson is about unusual vowel sounds.

You know the *patach* אַ vowel sounds like **AH** in m**a**tzah.

You know the *segol* אֶ vowel sounds like **EH** in m**e**lech.

You know the *sh'va* אְ vowel sounds silent or like a pause.

These new vowels join two vowels together.
The *sh'va* is silent, so the sounds of the *patach* and the *segol* are left!

אֲ

Chataf patach
Sounds like **AH**

אֱ

Chataf segol
Sounds like **EH**

READ WITH A TEACHER

Read these words from prayers:

<u>Real Prayers!</u>

1 אֱ-לֹ-הֵי-נוּ אֱלֹהֵינוּ בֶּ-אֱ-מֶ-ת בֶּאֱמֶת אֲ-שֶׁר אֲשֶׁר

2 הֲ-שִׁי-בֵ-נוּ הֲשִׁיבֵנוּ הָ-עֲ-בוֹ-דָה הָעֲבוֹדָה

הַ-נֶ-אֱ-מָן הַנֶּאֱמָן

3 יַ-עֲ-קֹב יַעֲקֹב חֲ-סִי-דָיו חֲסִידָיו זַר-עֲ-ךָ זַרְעֲךָ

Teacher's Signature _____

2 You know the *kamatz* אָ vowel sounds like **AH** in *matzah*.

★ Sometimes that vowel sounds like **OH**. Then it is called the *kamatz katan*. Some books help the reader by printing the *kamatz katan* like this אָ. The *kamatz katan* is important for grammar reasons that you will learn as you continue to study Hebrew. For now, you will have to practice and remember words that have that sound.

★ A *kamatz katan* אָ joins with the *sh'va* אְ to make a *chataf kamatz katan* אֳ. This vowel ALWAYS sounds like **OH**.

READING RULE 11

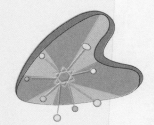

Chataf vowels have the same sound as the vowel without the sh'va:

אַ = אֲ = AH
patach = chataf patach

אֶ = אֱ = EH
segol = chataf segol

אָ = אֳ = OH
kamatz katan =
chataf kamatz katan

READ WITH A TEACHER

Read these words from prayers. The *kamatz katan* is printed like this:  אָ.

Real Prayers!

1 כָּל שֶׁ־בְּ־כָל שֶׁבְּכָל וּ־בְ־כָל וּבְכָל וּ־מִ־כָּל וּמִכָּל

2 עָ־נִי עָנִי אָ־נִ־יָּה אָנִיָּה צָ־הָ־רַ־יִם צָהֳרַיִם

3 קָד־שְׁ־ךָ קָדְשְׁךָ וּ־בְ־שָׁכְ־בְּ־ךָ וּבְשָׁכְבְּךָ

אֶכְ־תָּ־בֶ־נָּה אֶכְתָּבֶנָּה

Teacher's Signature _____

3 You know that when we read Hebrew:

1. We read from RIGHT to LEFT.

2. We say the CONSONANT FIRST and the vowel second.

THERE IS AN EXCEPTION!

If the **last letter and vowel of a word is** חַ **then we read the vowel first and then the letter.** We say ACH, not CHA.

Samei-ach = שָׂמֵחַ

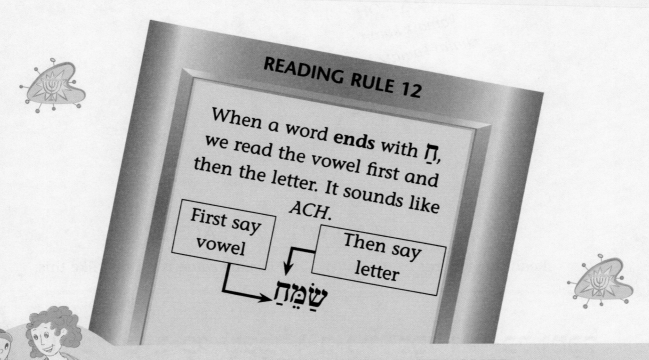

READING RULE 12

When a word **ends** with חַ, we read the vowel first and then the letter. It sounds like ACH.

First say vowel → שָׂמֵחַ ← Then say letter

READ WITH A TEACHER

Read these words from prayers. The *kamatz katan* is printed like this: אָ.

Real Words!

1 שָׂ-מֵ-חַ שָׂמֵחַ רוּ-חַ רוּחַ לְ-שַׁ-בֵּ-חַ לְשַׁבֵּחַ

2 מַצְ-מִי-חַ מַצְמִיחַ פּוֹ-תֵ-חַ פּוֹתֵחַ סוֹ-לֵ-חַ סוֹלֵחַ

1 Read the words with a friend. Circle the vowels in each line that make the sound shown in the box.

EH	לֶקַח אֵלֶיךָ אֱמֶת אֱמוּנָה שֶׁנִּשְׂרַף
AH	וַעֲנָיָו מִלְּפָנֶיךָ לַעֲמוֹד חָפֵץ וְנַעֲשֶׂה
OH	מִכָּל מִכֹּל אָהֳלֵי תִּרְדֹּף חָכְמָה

2 Match the sounds that are the same in both columns.

אֶל	___	עֵל	1
עַל	___	עֹל	2
אֵלוּ	___	עַל	3
עוֹל	___	אֵל	4
אָלוּ	___	עוֹלוּ	5

3 Circle the syllables where the vowel is read BEFORE the letter. It sounds like *ACH*.

אוֹרֶךְ אוֹרֵחַ אוֹרָה מְשִׁיחָה מָשִׁיחַ

מִזְבֵּחַ שִׂמְחַת שָׂמֵחַ כֹּחוֹ כֹּחַ

NOW YOU CAN READ THE SIDDUR סִדּוּר!! Lesson twenty is done! It's time to take home your award. Answers for this lesson are on page 89.

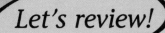

Let's review!

Lesson 21

READ WITH A TEACHER

REMEMBER: 1. We read Hebrew from RIGHT to LEFT.

2. Say the CONSONANT FIRST and the vowel second.

Right to Left Edition

THE HEBREW READER

Just for Kids

1   חֲנוּכָּה פּוּרִים פֶּסַח סֻכּוֹת רֹאשׁ הַשָּׁנָה

2   תּוֹרָה סִדּוּר הַגָּדָה בְּרָכָה אֶתְרוֹג לֶחֶם

3   אֲפִיקוֹמָן קְלָף צְדָקָה צִיצִית לוּלָב גִּבּוֹר

4   נָבִיא מְזוּזָה יָד יְרוּשָׁלַיִם וְצִוָּנוּ שָׂפָה

Real Prayers!

1   אֲשֶׁר בָּחַר בָּנוּ מִכָּל הָעַמִּים

2   מַצְמִיחַ קֶרֶן יְשׁוּעָה

3   יָאֵר יְיָ פָּנָיו אֵלֶיךָ וִיחֻנֶּךָּ

4   שִׁירָה חֲדָשָׁה שִׁבְּחוּ גְאוּלִים

5   שְׁמַע קוֹלֵנוּ יְיָ אֱלֹהֵינוּ חוּס וְרַחֵם עָלֵינוּ

1 Take out your *Alef-bet Letter Cards* ▢ to do these activities.

Find the letters that have the same sound even though they are different letters. (Do not use *sofit* (final) letters.) When you find them, write them here. There are six groups:

These letters _____ have the sound of_____.

These letters _____ have the sound of_____.

These letters _____ have the sound of_____.

These letters _____ have the sound of_____.

These letters _____ have the sound of_____.

These letters _____ have the sound of_____.

2 Find letters that are the same except for a dot (inside or above). There are five pairs. When you find them, write the letters and their sounds here:

_____ and _____   _____ and _____
letter/sound   letter/sound   letter/sound   letter/sound

_____ and _____   _____ and _____
letter/sound   letter/sound   letter/sound   letter/sound

_____ and _____
letter/sound   letter/sound

3 Find all of the *SOFIT* (FINAL) letters. When you find them, write them here:

1_____   2_____   3_____   4_____   5_____

67

4 Remember:

Find the letter groups that are families. When you find them, write them here:

Family 1 _____   Family 2 _____

Family 3 _____   Family 4 _____

Family 5 _____   Family 6 _____

Family 7 _____

5 There are letters that look alike but are not the same. Find letters that you sometimes confuse. Write them here with their sounds:

Group 1 _____   Group 2 _____
      letter/sound   letter/sound   letter/sound   letter/sound

Group 3 _____   Group 4 _____
      letter/sound   letter/sound   letter/sound   letter/sound

Group 5 _____
      letter/sound   letter/sound

Answers for this lesson are on pages 90–91. When you finish this lesson, take home your award!

READING RULE 1

Hebrew vowels go to the left of a consonant or under a consonant.

1 Put an X on words that are written wrong.

a אַ_דֹנָי אַדֹנָי עוֹלָם יְ·מְלוֹךְ

b אֱלֹהֵינוּ אֱלֹהֵינוּ וָ·עֶ·ד

READING RULE 2

Vowels cannot stand alone. Vowels have to be attached to consonants (except for וּ at the beginning of a word).

2 Circle the correct spelling of each pair.

a אוֹר וֹר

c הָאֶרֶץ הָ·רֶץ

b הָעוֹלָם הָעֹלָם

d הוֹדִיעַ הוֹדִ_

READING RULE 3

The letters ה and י are silent when they are not followed by a vowel.

3 Circle the letters that are SILENT.

a הָאֶרֶץ בָא יִרְעַם בְּצֶדֶק וְיוֹשְׁבֵי

b יְשׁוּעָה אַתָּה מְאֹד שִׁיר הַגּוֹיִם

READING RULE 4

Sofit letters can only appear at the **end of a word**. Their partner letters can only appear in the beginning or middle of a word.

4 Fill in the correct letter:

a לְחַיִּ_ ז_ן ם or מ

b מַלְ_וּת מֶלֶ_ כ or ך

c עֶ_ _ְדָקָה צ or ץ

d חַ_וּכָה גֶפֶ_ נ or ן

69

5 These are words you know. Fill in the missing vowels:

a   שַׁבָּת   אֲפִיקוֹמָן   פֵּרִים   בָּרוּךְ

b   לְחַיִּים   יִשְׂרָאֵל   שׁוֹפָר   מְנוֹרָה   מְזוּזָה

6 Look at the letter in the square. Circle the letters on each line that are in the same family.

ב   לְבָבְךָ   רַב   בִּימָה   שַׁבָּת   מְבֹרָךְ   בָּרוּךְ

כ   לָכֶם   לִבָּם   אֶכְרֹת   מִכָּל   בָּרוּךְ   בְּרָכָה

נ   וְאֵין   וְהָיוּ   מְצֻוְּךָ   זִכָּרוֹן   אָנֹכִי   נֵס

פ   פֶּסַח   בָּרוּךְ   כִּיפָּה   קְלָף   תְּפִילָה   סֵפֶר

צ   הָאָרֶץ   לְעוֹלָם   מִצְרַיִם   הוֹצֵאתִי   הָעֵץ

7 Circle all the double-duty dots:

a   נְחֹשֶׁת   קָדוֹשׁ   הַקֹּדֶשׁ   יִשְׂרָאֵל   מֹשֶׁה

b   שָׁלוֹם   שִׂמְחָה   חֹשֶׁךְ   וְשָׂשׂן   נָשָׂא

8 Divide each word into syllables:

More than one vowel per syllable?	Divided into syllables	WORD	
no	חַ־יִּים	חַיִּים	a
		מִצְוֹתָיו	b
		שֶׁבְּכָל	c
		קֹוֵינוּ	d
		שִׁוַּעְתִּי	e

70

READING RULE 9

When we see God's name, יְהֹוָה or יְיָ, we read it as Adonai אֲדֹנָי.

Some books use the letter 'ה in place of יְהֹוָה or יְיָ. We also read this as Adonai אֲדֹנָי.

9 Circle every word that we pronounce *Adonai.*

a בָּרוּךְ אַתָּה יְיָ, יִהְיוּ לְרָצוֹן יְהֹוָה צוּרִי

b שְׁמַע יִשְׂרָאֵל יְהֹוָה אֱלֹהֵינוּ, יְיָ צְבָאוֹת שְׁמוֹ

READING RULE 10

A דָּגֵשׁ does not change the sound of a letter unless the letter is:

פ - פּ

כ - כּ

ב - בּ

10 Find every letter with a דָּגֵשׁ.
Circle the letter if the דָּגֵשׁ changes the letter's sound.
Put an X on the letter if the דָּגֵשׁ does not change the sound.

a מְסַדֵּר מִפְּנֵי מֵבִיא הַמַּעֲרִיב מִכָּל מִמֶּנּוּ

b בְּשָׁכְבֵּנוּ אַתָּה נֶהְגֶּה חֻקִּים וְקַיָּם בָּרְכוּ

READING RULE 11

CHataf vowels have the same sound as the vowel without the *sh'va:*

אַ = אֲ = AH
patach = chataf patach

אֶ = אֱ = EH
segol = chataf segol

אָ = אֳ = OH
*kamatz katan =
chataf kamatz katan*

11 Circle the vowels that are *chataf* vowels.

a הַמַּעֲרִיב עֲרָבִים לֵילָה אֱלֹהֵינוּ וֶאֱמוּנָה

b אֲשֶׁר אֲנִי יְהֹוָה עֳנִי וְצׇהֳרַיִם מַלְאָכֵי

READING RULE 12

When a word **ends** with חַ, we read the vowel first and then the letter. It sounds like *ACH.*

First say vowel → Then say letter

שָׂמֵחַ

12 Circle the words that rhyme in each line.

a בָּרוּךְ פּוֹתֵחַ שָׁבוּעַ מְנַצֵּחַ הַפּוֹרֵחַ

b בְּרָכָה אֱלֹהֶיךָ שָׂמֵחַ שִׂמְחָה לִבָבֶךָ

c מִזְבֵּחַ יְשׁוּעָה מַלְאָךְ כֹּחַ בְּרָכָה

Answers for this lesson are on pages 91–93. When you finish this lesson, take home your award!
מַזָּל טוֹב!
You are ready for Ramah 3.

71

Reading Rules

READING RULE 4
LESSON 8

Sofit letters can only appear at the **end of a word.** Their partner letters can only appear in the beginning or middle of a word.

READING RULE 5
LESSON 11

All letters in a word **must have a vowel.** **Exceptions to this rule:** 1. The last letter of a word doesn't have to have a vowel. 2. The letters א and י can be in the middle of a word without a vowel.

READING RULE 6
LESSON 12

Letters in the same "family" can take each other's places.

They are the same letter in different forms.

READING RULE 10
LESSON 19

A *dageish* דָּגֵשׁ does not change the sound of a letter unless the letter is:

פּ – פ

כּ – כ

בּ – ב

READING RULE 11
LESSON 20

CHataf vowels have the same sound as the vowel without the *sh'va*:

אַ = אֲ = AH
patach = *chataf patach*

אֶ = אֱ = EH
segol = *chataf segol*

אָ = אֳ = OH
kamatz katan = *chataf kamatz katan*

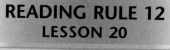

READING RULE 12
LESSON 20

When a word **ends** with חַ, we read the vowel first and then the letter it sounds like ACH.

First say vowel

שָׂמֵחַ

Then say letter

READING RULE 1
LESSON 1

Hebrew vowels go to the left of a consonant or under a consonant.

READING RULE 2
LESSON 4

Vowels cannot stand alone. Vowels have to be attached to consonants.

READING RULE 3
LESSON 5

The letters ה and י are silent when they are not followed by a vowel.

READING RULE 7
LESSON 15

The dot above a שׁ or שׂ can be a "double-duty dot."

Sometimes it serves as the dot for the letter AND a *cholam chaseir* vowel (אֹ).

READING RULE 8
LESSON 16

Each consonant can have only one vowel.

READING RULE 9
LESSON 18

When we see God's name, יְהֹוָה or יְיָ, we read it as *Adonai* אֲדֹנָי.

Some books use the letters ה׳ in place of יְהֹוָה or יְיָ. We also read this as *Adonai* אֲדֹנָי.

Reading Hebrew Rules!

73

Ramah 2 Answer Guide

Circle the parts of the words below that ARE VOWELS.

WITHOUT VOWELS	WITH VOWELS
Purim פרים	Purim פּוּרִים
Rosh HaShanah ראש השנה	Rosh HaShanah רֹאשׁ הַשָּׁנָה
Sukkot סכת	Sukkot סֻכּוֹת

1 Circle the VOWELS in these Hebrew words:

Shofar   שׁוֹפָר   Jerusalem   יְרוּשָׁלַיִם   Torah   תּוֹרָה

Challah   חַלָּה   Menorah   מְנוֹרָה

1 Find these letters: Underline every תּ and ת.
                         Circle every בּ.
                         Put an X on every ר.

ת	צ	בּ	תּ	ר	נ	ח	כ	בּ	ל	א
א	א	ק	ס	ל	ר	בּ	תּ	ג	מ	כ
שׁ	בּ	תּ	ד	י	תּ	ט	ע	תּ	פ	שׁ
צ	נ	שׁ	ד	נ	צ	פ	בּ	ר	ר	ג

Lesson 3

2 What are the sounds and names of consonants and vowels that you know? Fill in the chart. (You can use your *Alef-bet Chart* and your *Alef Advancer* ▢ to help!)

	Consonent or Vowel	Sound	Name	Write it:
ל	C	L	*lamed*	ל
מ	C	M	*mem*	מ
ַ	V	AH	*patach*	ַ
בּ	C	B	*bet*	בּ
ָ	V	AH	*kamatz*	ָ
שׁ	C	SH	*shin*	שׁ
פ	C	F	*fei*	פ
וֹ	V	OH	*cholam*	וֹ
ר	C	R	*reish*	ר

3 Match the Hebrew with the English sounds. Write the number in the blank.

1 Rah   **4**   בֶּת   4 Bet   **6**   רֵשׁ

2 Loh   **1**   רָ   5 Mor   **2**   לוֹ

3 Far   **5**   מוֹר   6 Resh   **3**   פַר

Lesson 4

1 Match the sounds:

1	Ah	5	לוֹ
2	Oh	7	בֵּ
3	Ah	1 or 3	אָ
4	Eh	4	אֱ
5	Loh	8	בֶּ
6	Shoh	2	אוֹ
7	Bah	6	שׁוֹ
8	Beh	1 or 3	אַ

2 Match these syllables to their sounds. You can check your answers by looking on the back!

אָ	אֱ	אוֹ	אַ
AH	EH	OH	AH
kamatz	*segol*	*cholam*	*patach*

Lesson 5

2 Take out these *Alef-bet Letter Cards* ☐ מ ר שׁ ל ב ת ה פ י. Take out these *Advancer Vowel Cards* ☐ ָ ֱ ָ ַ וֹ. Put together these sounds with the cards. You will use each card only once:

a) Mar — מַר or מָר

b) Shol — שׁוֹל

c) Bet — בֶּת

d) Heef — הִף

e) Yah — יָ or יַ

3 Circle the syllables that rhyme in each line:

a   בַּל לְפ מְפ בֵּל בְּפ שָׁב

b   אַת הָת פַּר בְּת אוֹל אַל

c   שֶׁל מֶשׁ יֵל שָׁשׁ אֶב יְל

d   מוֹב יֵב הוֹפ אוֹב יוֹב רָב

4 Read these syllables and words. Circle the silent consonants.

a   אוֹ פִּי יֶשׁ לָה הָל יְל לִי

b   תּוֹרָה אוֹרָה אָמוֹר אַבָּא מִילָה

c   בִּימָה שַׁבָּת שֶׁלִּי שֶׁלּוֹ שָׁלָה

Lesson 6

2 LOOK-ALIKE PAIRS: Some letters look alike. Check these out carefully.

ד	ר
Dalet	*Reish*
Sounds like **D**	Sounds like **R**

Circle every *dalet*. Put an X on every *reish*.

ד ר נ ך ד ר ז ו ד ר ד ו ד ך ד ר ד ד

ח	ה	ת
Chet	*Hei*	*Tav*
Sounds like **CH**	Sounds like **H**	Sounds like **T**

Circle every *CHet*. Put an X on every *hei*. Underline every *tav*:

ה ת ח ד ה ס ה ה ת ח ת ת ר ת ח ה ה

וֹ	וּ
Cholam	*Shuruk*
Sounds like OH in sh<u>o</u>far	Sounds like U in P<u>u</u>rim

Circle every *cholam*. Put an X on every *shuruk*:

ר וּ ז וֹ ו זּ וֹ ך ן וֹ ו וּ ז ר וֹ וּ

3 Letter review: Fill in the names and sounds of these consonants.

Lessons	א	ה	ד	ת	ל	שׁ	בּ
Name	alef	hei	dalet	tav	lamed	shin	bet
Sound	silent	H	D	T	L	SH	B

Lessons	ר	ח	פ	מ	י	ת
Name	reish	chet	fei	mem	yod	tav
Sound	R	CH	F	M	Y	T

4 Use your vowel ▢ and letter cards ▢ to make these syllables:

a. Mah מָה, מַה   Mee מִ, מִי   Mu מוּ

b. Lod לוֹד   Lahd לָד, לַד   Led לֵד

c. Heer הִיר, הִר   Hur הוּר   Har הָר, הַר

d. Et אֶת   Ot אוֹת   Ut (use the א) אוּת

e. Shub שׁוּב   Shob שׁוֹב   Sheeb שִׁיב, שִׁב

Lesson 7

2 Match the sounds:

1 Poh   2 Voh   3 Bee   4 Bu   5 Vu   6 Fu   7 Fei   8 Pei

פֵּ	8	בּוּ	4
בוּ	5	פּוֹ	1
פוּ	6	פֵ	7
בֹ	2	בּ	3

3 Circle the letter combinations in each line that sound the same:

a בִּימָה בְמָה בְּמַ בֵּמָה בְּמַה בֵּמַה

b חוּפָּה הוּפַ חוּפָה חוּפָּה תוּפַ חוּפָּא

c רְשֶׁת רֶשֶׁת דְּשֶׁת רֶשֶׁת רְשֶׁח רָשַׁת

d יוּפַד יוּפְּד יוּפְד יוּפַר יוּפִיד יוּפִּיד

Lesson 8

2 Remember: *Sofit* letters can only be at the **end of a word**. Their partner letters **can never be at the end of a word**. Fill in the blanks with the correct letters to spell these real words:

מ OR ם
Mem OR Mem Sofit

מָרוֹם	דָּרוֹם	בִּימָה	אֱמֶת	שָׁלוֹם	מַתִּיר
High place	South	Pulpit	Truth	Peace	Sets free

פ OR ף
Fei OR Fei Sofit

אַף	אֶלֶף	פֶּלֶא	יוֹפִי	חֵיפָה	רוֹפֵא
Nose	Thousand	Wonders	Beauty	Haifa	Heals

3 Take out these letter cards: ⬜ ב ב ת ר מ י ם א פ פ ף פ ה

Take out these vowel cards: 🟦 ⬜ אָ אֶ אֵ וּ אַ אֹ אֶ אֱ

Use these cards to make these sound combinations.
(There might be more than one way!)

a. Ba-lam	b. Ei-ruv	c. Bu-maf	d. To-rah
בַּלֶם ,בָּלַם ,בַּלַם	אֶרֶב ,אֵרוּב	בּוּמַף ,בְּמַף ,בּוּמָף	תּוֹרָה ,תּוֹרָה

e. Bee-pat	f. Tee-reif	g. Hu-mor	h. Mu-fah
בִּיפַת ,בְּפַת ,בִּפָת	תֵּרֵף ,תִּירֵף	הוּמוֹר ,הָמוֹר	מוּפָה ,מְפַה ,מְפָה

Lesson 9

2 *Vowel review!* Take out your *Alef Advancer* 🟦. Read these syllables.
Use your *Alef Advancer* to check yourself.

אֶ	אוּ	אָ	אֱ	אוֹ	אִ	אֵ	אַ
EH	U	AH	U	OH	EE	EI	AH

Now use your *Alef Advancer* to fill in the names of the vowels:

VOWEL: ‌ˍˍ *tseirei* ‌וּ *shuruk* ‌ˍ *kubutz* ‌ָ *kamatz*

‌וֹ *cholam* ‌ˍ *segol* ‌ˍ *patach* ‌ˍ *chirik*

3 Circle the letters in each line that match the letter in the box:

⟨פ⟩	ב	ב	⟨פ⟩	כ	כ	ב	⟨פ⟩	פ	כ	⟨פ⟩	ב	כ	ב	**פ**	a
פ	⟨ב⟩	פ	⟨ב⟩	פ	כ	כ	⟨ב⟩	פ	פ	כ	⟨ב⟩	כ	⟨ב⟩	**ב**	b
פ	ב	כ	⟨כ⟩	⟨כ⟩	ב	פ	פ	⟨כ⟩	פ	ב	⟨כ⟩	כ	ב	**כ**	c
⟨ד⟩	ר	⟨ד⟩	ה	⟨ד⟩	ר	ו	ר	⟨ד⟩	ר	⟨ד⟩	ר	ח	⟨ד⟩	**ד**	d

4 Add the letter בּ to these words.

Read the words with a friend.

מְנוֹרָה	נֵר	נָבִיא	דַיֵּנוּ
Lamp	Candle	Prophet	Enough for us!

5 Draw line to match the words:

Pizza

Tzedakah

HaMotzi

Beitzah

Tzitzit

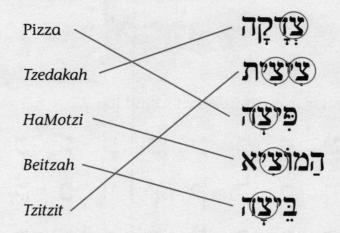

צְדָקָה

צִיצִת

פִּיצָה

הַמוֹצִיא

בֵּיצָה

Circle all of the letters that are *TZadi* צ in the words above.

Lesson 10

2 Fill in the blanks with the correct letters to spell these real words:

Remember: *Sofit* letters can only be at the **end of a word**.
Their partner letters **can never be at the end of a word**.

ן נ
or
Nun or *Nun Sofit*

מִפִּינוּ	רַחֲמָן	בָּנִים	נֶצַח	נָבִיא	צִיּוֹן

ך כ
or
CHaf or *CHaf Sofit*

כָּמוֹכָה	מֶלֶךְ	בְּכָל	דֶרֶךְ	אֶתְכֶם	בָּרוּךְ

ץ צ
or
TZadi or *TZadi Sofit*

רָצוֹן	אוֹמֵץ	צוּר	אֶרֶץ	מִצְרַיִם	צִיּוֹן

81

3 Draw lines connecting the letters to their partners:

ד ף ן ס ץ

נ פ כ צ מ

2 Circle the letters in each line that sound like K.

ⓚ ב מ ⓟ ⓚ ⓚ פ ⓚ נ נ ⓚ כ נ כ ⓚ a

ד ⓠ ף ⓠ ל ⓠ ץ ד כ ⓠ ף ל ד ⓠ b

ⓠ ב ⓚ ⓚ כ ⓠ ח פ ⓚ פ ⓠ ⓚ נ ב c

3 Match the words to the pictures:

צְדָקָה

חֲנֻכָּה

כִּפָּה

אֲפִיקוֹמָן

פְּרִי

4 Fill in the *SH'VA* vowel wherever it is needed. Use Reading Rule 5 at the bottom of page 36 to complete this activity.

פְּרִי	צִיצִית	בְּרָכָה	יִצְחָק
Fruit	Fringes	Blessing	Isaac

בְּרֵאשִׁית	תְּפִילָה	קְלָף	צֵאתְכֶם
Beginning	Prayer	Parchment	Your going out

5 Put a circle around each *sh'va* that is a **pause**.

Put an X on each *sh'va* that is **silent**.

For example:

לְחַיִּים   אַבְרָהָם   הַבְדָּלָה   מְנוֹרָה

נִקְרָא   לִפְנֵי   תְּפִילָה   מַלְכוּת   יְרוּשָׁלַיִם   קְהִילָה

פְּרִי   מִצְרַיִם   לְבָבְךָ   בְּמָקוֹם   לְכָה   בְּצִיּוֹן

Lesson 12

2 Take out these *Alef-bet Letter Cards*: ▇

ץ פ ס ן ם צ מ ף כ ן ד ב כ נ ב פ בּ כ

a Organize them into their family groups.

צ-ץ   מ-ם   נ-ן   כ-כ-ך   פ-פ-ף   ב-בּ

b Do you know all of their names. Use your *Alef-bet Chart* or your *Alef Advancer* ▨ letter strips to check your answers.

כ	ב	פ	בּ	ך	נ	כּ
CHaf	vet	fei	bet	CHaf sofit	nun	kaf

ף	צ	מ	ן	ם	פּ	ץ
fei sofit	TZadi	mem	nun sofit	mem sofit	pei	TZadi sofit

c Take out all of the *SOFIT* letters. There are five. Match them to their partner letters that appear in the middle or beginning of a word.

כ-ך   מ-ם   נ-ן   פ-ף   צ-ץ

3 Circle the letter combinations in each line that have the SAME SOUND:

a בָּרוּן כָדוּן כַּדוֹנ קַדוּן קַדוֹן קָרוּן כָדוּן בָּדוּם

b פְּבֵּץ פְּבֶצ פִּיבֵף פְּבֵף פִּיבֶץ פִּיבֵך מִיבֵץ

c בּוּכְם כּוּבֵם כְּבֵם בּוּבֵם בּוּבֵם כְּפֵם כּוּבֵם

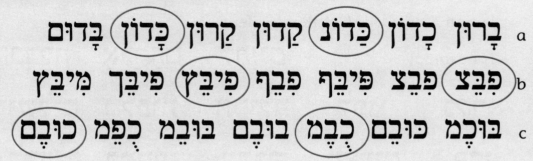

Lesson 13

2 Circle all the letters in each line that match the sound of the English letter:

Sounds like T	ת ט ד ת כ ת ט ת שׁ ת ט צ ט
Sounds like T	ט מ ב ט ע שׁ ט מ ס ט פ ט
Sounds silent	א ח ע ע ך א מ ע ץ ר א ע
Sounds silent	ע ג צ ע ק ף ע א צ ע ע מ
Sounds like G	ד ג ה נ ג כ ג נ ת י ג ן

3 Match the syllables that sound the same.
Write the number in the blank:

3 תַּגָא	תּוֹם 1
5 כֵּרוֹם	עוֹד 2
4 מֹנֵע	טַגָה 3
6 רֵעוֹת	מוֹנֶה 4
2 אַד	קֵרֹם 5
1 טֹם	רַאְט 6

2 You know all of the vowels on your *Alef Advancer* ▮ strip! Use your *Alef Advancer* to review the names and sounds of the vowels. Then fill in this chart:

Name	*patach*	*kamatz*	*shuruk*	*sh'va*	*segol*	*kubutz*	*cholam*	*tzeirei*	*chirik*	*cholam chaseir*
Looks like	–	ָ	וּ	ְ	ֶ	ֻ	וֹ	ֵ	ִ	ֹ
Sounds like	AH	AH	U	silent pause	EH	U	OH	EI	EE	OH

3 Circle the letters in each line that have the same sound as the English letter:

S   שׁ שׂ ש שׁ ס ט ש שׁ ם ס ת פ ס ס שׁ ם ש שׁ שׂ

Z   ס ו וֹ צ ז ן ז ר ס ץ ז וֹ ד שׁ ז י ס וּ

TZ   ן צ ף ץ ע שׂ ז ע שׁ צ ע ז ס ע ף צ ו

1 Circle all the letters that are שׁ. Underline all the letters that are שׂ.

עֹשֶׂה   יְחֶשֹׂף   קָדוֹשׁ   שָׂרה   שְׁלֹשֶׁת

שׁוֹפָר   שָׁשָׁן   יֹשְׁבֵי   יְטֹשׁ   יִשְׂרָאֵל

2 Circle the dots that are "double-duty dots." (These dots are BOTH a *cholam chaseir* vowel AND the dot for the letters שׂ or שׁ.)

שִׂמְחָה   יְחֶשֹׂף   רֹאשׁ   שֹׁשָׁן   קָדוֹשׁ

לִפְרוֹשׁ   שִׁמּוּשׁ   נָשֹׂא   נְחֹשֶׁת   לִפְרֹשׂ

2 Circle all the letters that sound like V.

ו (ו) (ב) (ו) (ו) ב י (ב) (ו) כ (ו) (ב) (ב) (ו) (ו) ו

ו ן (ו) (ו) ז ד (ו) ז (ו) ר (ו) ז ן ד (ו) ז ז

3 In the words below:

Circle the ו‎s that are CONSONANTS. Underline the ו‎s that are VOWELS.

a צוּרִי מִצְוָה מִצְוֹת בְּמִצְוֹתָיו בְּמְרוֹמָיו

b צִיּוֹן צִיּוֹנוֹת וְצִוְּנוּ וְהֶגְיוֹן וְאָהַבְתָּ

c דּוֹד דָּוִד דּוֹר דּוֹרָיו לְעוֹלָם וָעֶד

5 Use your *Alef-bet Letter Chart* to help you put all of the consonants in alphabetical order.

א ב ב ג ד ה ו ז ח ט י כ כ ך ל מ מ ם נ נ ן ס ע פ פ ף צ ץ ק ר ש ש ת ת

1 *ON YOUR OWN*

Circle the sound combinations and words that rhyme in each line.

a (שְׂפָתַי) (לְפָנַי) לְפָנָיו שְׁבִיעִי נְבִיאֵי

b גָּלוּ (גָּלוּי) (מַשּׂוּי) שְׁמוֹ שְׁמִי

c אוֹיֵב סְאוּ (סְעוּי) וְגוֹי (וְגוֹי)

d (אֲבוֹתַי) לַחַיִּים (מִצְוֹתַי) עָשׂוּי אוֹי

86

2 Unscramble the words below to create the שְׁמַע prayer.
Write the words in the correct order.

שְׁמַע יִשְׂרָאֵל אַדֹנָי אֱלֹהֵינוּ אַדֹנָי אֶחָד

3 You know many blessings that begin

בָּרוּךְ אַתָּה אַדֹנָי אֱלֹהֵינוּ מֶלֶךְ הָעוֹלָם

Read each line below. There are TWO mistakes in each line. Circle them:

a בָּרוּךְ אֶתָּה אַדֹנָי אֱלֹהֵינוּ טֶלֶךְ הָעוֹלָם

b בָּרוּךְ אַדֹנָי אַתָּה אֱלֹהֵינוּ מֶלֶךְ הָעוֹלָם

c בָּרוּךְ אַתָּה אַדֹנָי אֱלֹהֵינוּ מֶלֶךְ הָעוֹלָם

d בָּרוּךְ אַתָּה אַדֹנָי אֱלֹהֵינוּ מֶלֶךְ הָעוֹלָם

Lesson 18

1 In the lines below, circle each name of God that we **pronounce** *Adonai*.

a בָּרוּךְ אַתָּה יְיָ אֱלֹהֵינוּ מֶלֶךְ הָעוֹלָם

b שְׁמַע יִשְׂרָאֵל יְהֹוָה אֱלֹהֵינוּ יְהֹוָה אֶחָד

c רְצֵה יְיָ אֱלֹהֵינוּ

d יִמְלֹךְ יְהֹוָה לְעוֹלָם

1 You know these pairs of "sister" letters. Write their names and sounds below them:

פ – פּ	כ – כּ	ב – בּ

Sound	F – P	CH – K	V – B
Name	*fei – pei*	*chaf – kaf*	*vet – bet*

1 In the מִי כָמֹכָה prayer below:

⭐ Put a circle around the letters with a דָּגֵשׁ **if the sound changes.**

⭐ Put an X on the letters with a דָּגֵשׁ **if the sound does not change.**

מִי־כָמֹכָה בָּאֵלִים, יְיָ?

מִי כָּמֹכָה, נֶאְדָּר בַּקֹּדֶשׁ,

נוֹרָא תְהִלֹּת, עֹשֵׂה פֶלֶא?

שִׁירָה חֲדָשָׁה שִׁבְּחוּ גְאוּלִים לְשִׁמְךָ עַל־שְׂפַת הַיָּם; יַחַד כֻּלָּם

הוֹדוּ וְהִמְלִיכוּ וְאָמְרוּ: "יְיָ יִמְלֹךְ לְעֹלָם וָעֶד!"

2 Circle any מֶתֶג that you find in the מִי כָמֹכָה prayer below.

מִי־כָמֹכָה בָּאֵלִים, יְיָ?

מִי כָּמֹכָה, נֶאְדָּר בַּקֹּדֶשׁ,

נוֹרָא תְהִלֹּת, עֹשֵׂה פֶלֶא?

שִׁירָה חֲדָשָׁה שִׁבְּחוּ גְאוּלִים לְשִׁמְךָ עַל־שְׂפַת הַיָּם; יַחַד כֻּלָּם

הוֹדוּ וְהִמְלִיכוּ וְאָמְרוּ: "יְיָ יִמְלֹךְ לְעֹלָם וָעֶד!"

What does the מֶתֶג do to the way we read the word?

It does not change the sound. It tells us where to put the accent

88

1 Read the words with a friend. Circle the vowels in each line that make the sound shown in the box.

EH	לָקַח אֵלֶיךָ אֱמֶת אֱמוּנָה שֶׁנִּשְׂרַף
AH	וַעֲנִיָּיו מִלְּפָנֶיךָ לַעֲמוֹד חָפֵץ וְנַעֲשֶׂה
OH	מִכָּל מִכֹּל אָהֳלֵי תִּרְדֹּף חָכְמָה

2 Match the sounds that are the same in both columns.

אֶל	1	עֱל	1
עָל	3	עֹל	2
אֱלוּ	2	עַל	3
עוֹל	4	אָל	4
אָלוּ	5	עֹלוּ	5

3 Circle the syllables where the vowel is read BEFORE the letter. It sounds like *ACH*.

אוֹרֶךָ אוֹרַח אוֹרָה מְשִׁיחָה מָשִׁיחַ

מִזְבֵּחַ שִׂמְחַת שָׂמַח כּוֹחוֹ כּוֹחַ

1 Take out your *Alef-bet Letter Cards* ▯ to do these activities.

Find the letters that have the same sound even though they are different letters. (Do not use *sofit* (final) letters.) When you find them, write them here. There are six groups:

These letters ב, ו   have the sound of V.

These letters א, ע   have the sound of silent.

These letters ח, כ, ך   have the sound of CH.

These letters ט, ת, ת   have the sound of T.

These letters ס, שׂ   have the sound of S.

These letters כ, ק   have the sound of K.

2 Find letters that are the same except for a dot (inside or above). There are five pairs. When you find them, write the letters and their sounds here:

בּ B		ב V		כּ K		כ CH
letter/sound	and	letter/sound		letter/sound	and	letter/sound

פּ P		פ F		תּ T		ת T
letter/sound	and	letter/sound		letter/sound	and	letter/sound

שׁ SH		שׂ S
letter/sound	and	letter/sound

3 Find all of the *SOFIT* (FINAL) letters. When you find them, write them here:

1 ך   2 ם   3 ן   4 ף   5 ץ

90

4 Find the letter groups that are families. When you find them, write them here:

Family 1   בּ,   ב   Family 2   כּ,   ך,   כ

Family 3   ם,   מ   Family 4   ן,   נ

Family 5   ף,   פּ,   פ   Family 6   ץ,   צ

Family 7   תּ,   ת

5 There are letters that look alike but are not the same. Find letters that you sometimes confuse. Write them here with their sounds. Here are some suggestions:

Group 1   ב/B   ב/V   כּ/K   פּ/P   כ/CH   פ/F   Group 2   נ/N   ז/Z   ו/V   י/Y

Group 3   ד/D   ר/R   ך/CH   Group 4   ת/T   ח/CH   ה/H

Group 5   צ/TZ   ע/silent   Group 6   ט/T   מ/M

Group 7   ם/M   ס/S   Group 8   נ/N   ג/G

Lesson 22

1 Put an X on words that are written wrong.

a   אַ־דֹנָי   אֲדֹנָי   עוֹלָם   י־מְלֹוךְ

b   אֱלֹהֵינוּ   לֹהֵינוּ   וָ־עֶ־ד

2 Circle the correct spelling of each pair.

a   אוֹר   וֹר   c   הָאָרֶץ   הָ־רֶץ

b   הָעוֹלָם   הָוֹלָם   d   הוֹדִיעַ   הֹדִ־

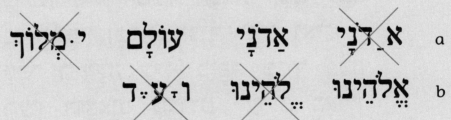

3 Circle the letters that are SILENT.

a הָאָ͏רֶץ בָּא יִרְעַ͏ם בְּצֶדֶק וְיוֹשְׁבֵ͏י

b יְשׁוּעָ͏ה אַתָּ͏ה מְאֹ͏ד שִׁיר הַגּוֹיִם

4 Fill in the correct letter:

a לְחַיִּים זְמַ_ ם or מ

b מַלְכוּת מֶלֶ_ ך or כ

c עֵ_ צְדָקָה ץ or צ

d חֲנֻכָּה גֶּפֶ_ ן or נ

5 These are words you know. Fill in the missing vowels:

a בָּרוּךְ פּוּרִים אֲפִיקוֹמָן שַׁבָּת

b מְזוּזָה מְנוֹרָה שׁוֹפָר יִשְׂרָאֵל לְחַיִּים

6 Look at the letter in the square. Circle the letters on each line that are in the same family.

ב בָּרוּךְ מְכִבְדֶךָ שַׁבָּת בִּימָה רָב לְבָבֶן

כ בְּרָכָה בָּרוּךְ מִכָּל אֶכֹת לִבָם לָכֶם

נ נֵס אֲנֹכִי זִכָּרוֹן מִצְוֶךָ וְהָיוּ וְאֵין

פ כַּפּוֹ תְּפִלָּה קְלָף כִּפָּה בָּרוּךְ פֶּסַח

צ הָעֵץ הוֹצֵאתִי מִצְוֹתָיו לְעוֹלָם הָאָרֶץ

7 Circle all the double-duty dots:

a מֹשֶׁה יִשְׂרָאֵל הַקֹּדֶשׁ קָדוֹשׁ נְחֹשֶׁת

b נָשָׂא וְשָׂשֹׂן חוֹשֶׁךְ שִׂמְחָה שָׁלוֹם

8 Divide each word into syllables:

More than one vowel per syllable?	Divided into syllables	WORD	
no	חַ-יִּים	חַיִּים	a
no	מִצְ-וֹ-תָיו	מִצְוֹתָיו	b
no	שֶׁ-בְּ-כָל	שֶׁבְּכָל	c
no	קָ-וִּי-נוּ	קִוִּינוּ	d
no	שִׁ-וַּעְ-תִּי	שִׁוַּעְתִּי	e

9 Circle every word that we pronounce *Adonai*.

a בָּרוּךְ אַתָּה ⟨יְיָ⟩, יִהְיוּ לְרָצוֹן ⟨יְהֹוָה⟩ צוּרִי

b שְׁמַע יִשְׂרָאֵל ⟨יְהֹוָה⟩ אֱלֹהֵינוּ, ⟨יְיָ⟩ צְבָאוֹת שְׁמוֹ

10 Find every letter with a דָּגֵשׁ.
Circle the letter if the דָּגֵשׁ changes the letter's sound.
Put an X on the letter if the דָּגֵשׁ does not change the sound.

a מִסֵּ֓ד מִפְּנֵי מֵבִיא הַמַּעֲרִיב מִכָּל מִמֶּ֓נּוּ

b בְּשָׁכְבְּנוּ אַתָּה נֶהֱגֶה חֻקִּים וְקַיָּם בָּרְכוּ

11 Circle the vowels that are *chataf* vowels.

a הַמַּעֲרִיב עֲרָבִים לַיְלָה אֱלֹהֵינוּ וֶאֱמוּנָה

b אֲשֶׁר אֲנִי יְהֹוָה עֳנִי וְצָהֳרַיִם מַלְאֲכֵי

12 Circle the words that rhyme in each line.

a בָּרוּךְ ⟨פּוֹתֵחַ⟩ ⟨שָׁבוּעַ⟩ ⟨מְנַצֵּחַ⟩ ⟨הַפּוֹרֵחַ⟩

b ⟨בְּרָכָה⟩ ⟨אֱלֹהֶיךָ⟩ שָׂמֵחַ ⟨שִׂמְחָה⟩ לְבָבֶךָ

c מִזְבֵּחַ יְשׁוּעָה ⟨מַלְאָךְ⟩ ⟨כֹּחַ⟩ ⟨בְּרָכָה⟩

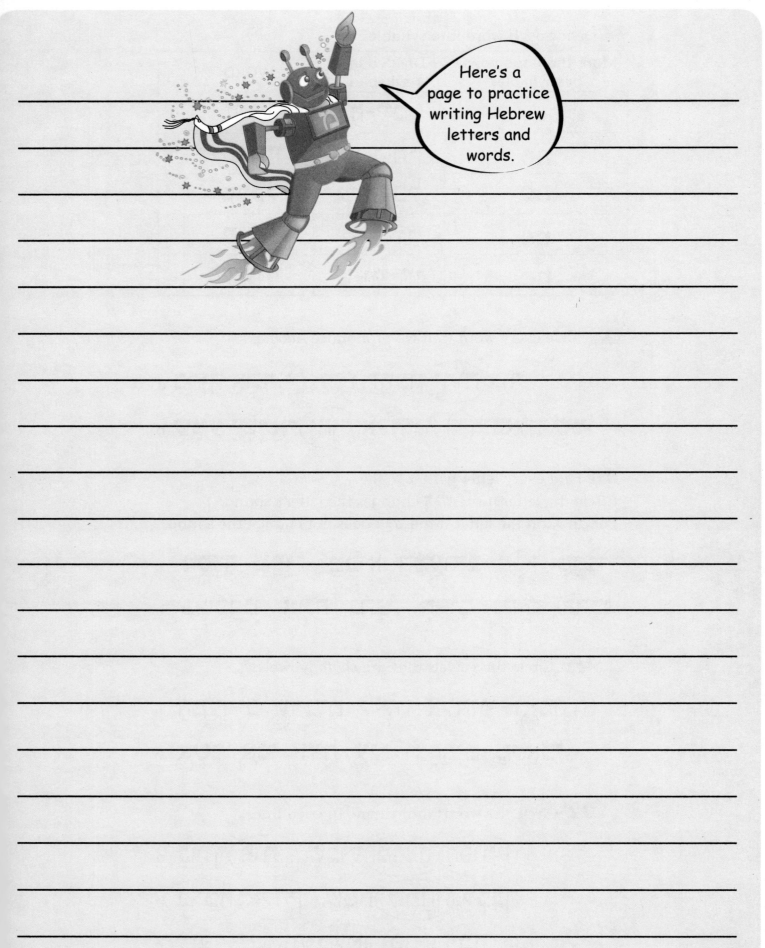

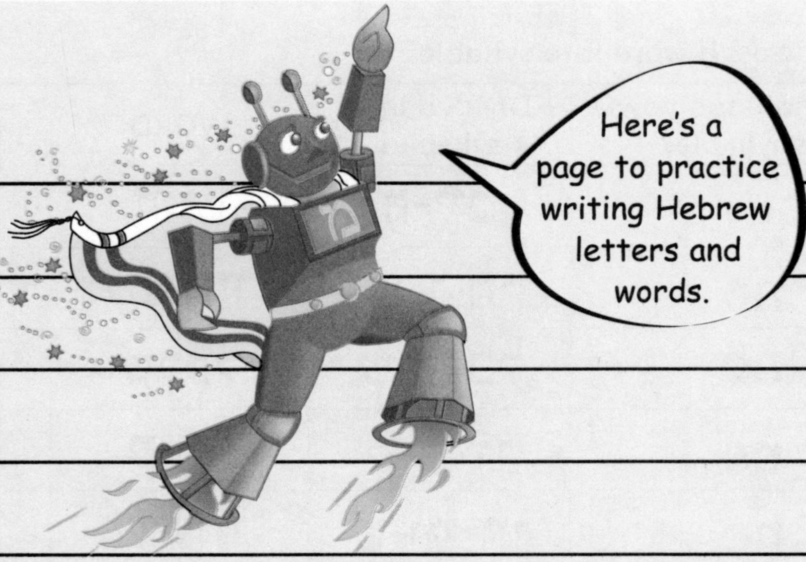
Here's a page to practice writing Hebrew letters and words.

Mitty's Lesson Award FLIP BOOK

© 2003 UAHC Press

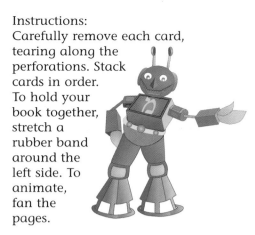

Instructions:
Carefully remove each card, tearing along the perforations. Stack cards in order. To hold your book together, stretch a rubber band around the left side. To animate, fan the pages.

You finished **Lesson 1!** You can read the word שׁוֹפָר!

You finished **Lesson 2!** You have learned the consonants בּ, תּ, ת, and the vowel אָ.

You finished **Lesson 3!** You have learned the consonants מ, ל, and the vowel אֱ.

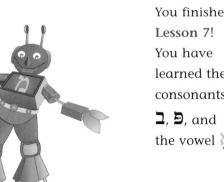

You finished **Lesson 4!** You have learned the silent letter א!

You finished **Lesson 5!** You have learned the consonants י, ה, and the vowel אֵ.

You finished **Lesson 6!** You have learned the consonants ד, ח, and the vowel וֹ.

You finished **Lesson 7!** You have learned the consonants בּ, פּ, and the vowel אֵ.

You finished **Lesson 8!** You have learned the final letters ם, ף, and the vowel אֱ.

You finished **Lesson 9!** You have learned the consonants כּ, נ, and כ.

You finished **Lesson 10!** You have learned the final letters ך, ן, and ץ.